The Technology of
FLY RODS

*An In-Depth Look at the Design
of the Modern Fly Rod,
Its History and Its Role in Fly Fishing*

By Don Phillips

Foreword by Ernest Schwiebert

D1597169

Frank
Amato
PORTLAND

About the Author

Don Phillips was born in Chattanooga, Tennessee in 1933, but he was brought up in Springfield, Massachusetts and spent his working life in north-central Connecticut. He is married to Dee, his wife of fifteen years, and has four children and ten grandchildren.

Don graduated from Technical High School in Springfield, and went on to receive a Bachelor of Science degree in Mechanical Engineering from the University of Massachusetts and a Master of Science degree in Business Management from the Hartford Graduate Center.

He worked for the Hamilton Standard division of United Technologies Corporation for over thirty-three years, holding various positions in Engineering, Marketing, Planning and Administration. While still working full time, he designed and developed the world's first fly rod made from boron fibers, and went on to form his own company, producing over 700 rods and blanks under the FlyCraft® label. He received two U.S. patents related to composite material fly rod design.

Don has written many feature articles for most of the major fly-fishing magazines and he is an FFF-Certified Casting Instructor.

Retired since 1989, Don lives on Marco Island, Florida, where he fishes, golfs, writes and travels extensively.

All inquiries should be addressed to:
Frank Amato Publications, Inc.
P.O. Box 82112 • Portland, Oregon 97282 • 503-653-8108
www.amatobooks.com

Book Design: Amy Tomlinson
Photography: Don Phillips, unless otherwise noted
Cover Photography: Doug Swisher

Printed in Hong Kong
1 3 5 7 9 10 8 6 4 2

Softbound ISBN: 1-57188-190-5   Softbound UPC: 0-66066-00401-7
Hardbound ISBN: 1-57188-191-3   Hardbound UPC: 0-66066-00402-4

Table of CONTENTS

List of
DRAWINGS & ILLUSTRATIONS

ACKNOWLEDGMENTS

Although it took most of the past year to write this book, the foundation for its content was laid decades earlier as both my engineering training and my fly-fishing skills matured. It is thus a most daunting task to thank all of the people who have helped me to put forward this writing. At the same time, reviewing my associations over the past forty years has been a most pleasurable and rewarding journey. I only hope that I haven't omitted some key individuals due to the sometimes fuzzy recollections from my sixty-five-year-old mind.

At the beginning, I must thank the Mechanical Engineering staff at the University of Massachusetts, who laid the framework for a life of technical learning. The discipline and skills of the late Professor Joe Marcus were particularly important in emphasizing the need to do things right, the first time. Also, my family deserves many thanks for their patience and understanding while I buried myself in the basement workshop or waded the streams of New England in search of knowledge and trout.

My sincerest thanks to the employees of United Technologies Corporation who, during the 1970s, put up with my incessant questions and provided those answers which have helped to unlock the secrets of the fly rod. Especially, my boss for many years, the late Don Richards and co-workers Walt Arnoldi, Stan Best, Charlie Brahm, Bob Cornell, Alan Cohen, Frank Galasso, Don Kuehl, Dick Novak, the late Roy Paul and Ed Rothman. My thanks also to the members of the Battenkill Fly Fishers, the Connecticut Fly Fisherman's Association and the Farmington River Anglers' Association, who at various times were sounding boards, guinea pigs and fly-rod customers.

My deepest thanks to Doug Swisher, close friend and fishing buddy, who really taught me what fly-casting was all about, who did the photo work for the cover and who was steadfast in encouraging me in my boron fly-rod development effort. Other notable individuals whose encouragement maintained my enthusiasm for boron fly rods were the late Wes Jordan, the late Sewell Dunton, the late Lee Wulff, the late Vince Marinaro, John Merwin, Silvio Calabi, Carl Richards, Dave Whitlock and Don Zahner.

While working with various fly-rod makers over the years, I received considerable advice and assistance from Walt Carpenter when he was with Payne, the late Tom Maxwell of Thomas & Thomas, Ron Kusse when he was with Leonard, Russ Peak, Hoagy B. Carmichael, Jim Green of Fenwick, Don Green of Sage, Steve Rajeff of G. Loomis, Jim Murphy of Redington and especially Leigh and Perk Perkins, Bill Cairns, the late Howard Steere, Tom Rosenbauer, Jim LePage and Jim Logan of Orvis. I really can't thank these individuals enough for the knowledge which they have shared with me.

Over the past year many individuals have helped me make this book project come to life. First, Nick Lyons of Lyons Press who helped convince me that this book should be written and published, and Frank Amato and Kim Koch of Frank Amato Publications who made it happen. Don and Kathy Bernier helped me in setting up line-loading experiments. My wife Dee and my daughter Karen Miller spent many hours with me unearthing patent information from various repositories. Paul Schullery, Mel Krieger, Andy Puyano and Ken Cameron were most helpful in filling in some of the pieces of the historical puzzle. Ernest Schwiebert, Doug Swisher, Tom Dorsey of Thomas & Thomas, Barry Beck, Dave Engerbretson and Mel Krieger all agreed to review the manuscript and add their wisdom to the final product. Dale Clemens added his considerable experience on the subject of fly-rod components. And finally, Graig Spolek, Ed Mosser and John Robson have provided technical material which has helped to round out coverage of the subject. My thanks to all of these individuals for their help in putting together the final product.

And of course, my deepest thanks and love to my wife, Dee; without whose love, support and patience this project would never have been completed.

Unless otherwise specified, all drawings and photographs are by the author. My sincerest thanks to these other sources who permitted their illustrations to be used in this book.

Source	Illustration
Ernest G. Schwiebert (from *Trout*)	Egyptian and Assyrian Art
Dame Juliana Berners (from her *Treatyse*)	Fishing Scene Woodcut
U.S. Patent Office	Chapters 2 & 3 Patent Illustrations
Carl Caiati and Tom Green	Chapter 2 Rod Component Closeup Photos

Source	Illustration
Paul Schullery (From *American Fly Fishing*)	Chapter 2 Rod Splice & Louis Rhead Dwg
Graig Spolek	Figures 9-13 and 10-1
Ed Mosser, Bill Buchman and Rod Walinchus	Figures 9-15 and 9-17
Jim LePage and the Orvis Company	Figure 10-2
Hoagy B. Carmichael and Everett Garrison	Figure 10-3
A.J. McClane and Henry Holt	Figures 4-3, 4-5, 4-6, 4-12 and 8-7

FOREWORD

Twenty-seven years have passed since I first met Don Phillips.

I first encountered carbon fiber rods when Andre Puyans of San Francisco and James Green, the great tournament caster whose contributions at both Fenwick and Sage are well known, introduced me to graphite at Sun Valley in 1973.

In those years, I was still a contributing editor at *Sports Afield* with my old friends and colleagues, Lee Wulff and Gene Adkins Hill. Don Green of Fenwick supplied me with a prototype graphite rod in Seattle that fall, and I fished it hard with Puyans, on big autumn chinook in Northern California. The prototype was fished again the following spring, on the steelhead of the Pere Marquette, with biologist Dave Borgerson of Michigan. The remarkable potential of carbon fiber was obvious, and I published an article on these new rods that appeared in *Sports Afield*.

Although Don Phillips had first drawn my attention to such aerospace fibers, with an article that introduced both graphite and boron technology in *Fly Fisherman* at Christmas in 1973, the piece which appeared a few weeks later in *Sports Afield* was the first to explore the potential of such exotic materials in a major outdoor periodical.

Through a complete accident of military proximity, I had first been introduced to carbon and boron fiber technology almost twenty years before, in the research laboratories at Wright-Patterson Air Force Base in Dayton, Ohio. Carbon graphite fibers are derived from petrochemical yarns, reducing their acrylonitrile fibers to their carbon constituents, and the process of manufacturing such fabric evolved from the work of Cortauld in the United Kingdom.

Such British research was commissioned and sustained by the Royal Aircraft Establishment, the British counterpart of the Air Force Research & Development Center at Wright-Patterson. The ground-breaking research involving boron fibers was first performed by Texaco, with the clandestine support of the Central Intelligence Agency.

Both carbon graphite and boron, combined with new adhesives and honeycomb structural concepts, had already demonstrated remarkable potential that let to the exotic performance of the SR-71 *Blackbird*. It was developed to provide high-altitude reconnaissance for both the Strategic Air Command and the CIA, and was originally conceived to replace the better-known Lockheed U-2.

Both organizations soon became fascinated with the possibility of a generation of new fighters and bombers. The potential of carbon graphite and boron for the so-called stealth technology has further evolved in the Northrup B-2 strategic bomber, and is paramount in the remarkable new Lockheed YF-22A fighter. The potential of boron and graphite for exotic aircraft performance and stealth technology has been widely known in the aerospace community for more than forty years, and most people are surprised to learn that the F-117A was first tested at Groom Lake in 1981.

Few anticipated other uses for boron and graphite.

Despite the exaggerated claims of some tackle manufacturers, it should have been obvious to the fly-fishing fraternity that most carbon fiber fabric was being produced for aerospace applications, and it was tailored entirely to the needs of that industry. Acres of carbon-fiber cloth are used in the construction of advanced military aircraft, while square inches of material are involved in fishing rods and golf shafts. There were only two general types of graphite available to rod manufacturers, during all the hyperbole over modulus of elasticity in recent years, although proprietary types of graphite existed only in the minds of the copywriters who happily seduced the angling world.

Don Phillips was among the pioneers who first worked with such exotic new materials, at the Hamilton Standard division of the United Technologies Corporation in Hartford, Connecticut.

Phillips was involved in the design and development of aircraft propellers, space suits, and other high-tech products at Hamilton Standard, but he also enjoyed a fly-fishing heritage, since both his grandfather and his father were devoted to the sport. The properties of boron and graphite held obvious potential for fishing rods, in his mind, and using potshards of scrap material discarded in the research facilities at Hartford, Phillips became the first to experiment with boron in the design and fabrication of fly rods, in late 1971.

Although many rod makers have reputedly been engineers, that supposition is largely founded on a mythology sustained by fishing writers and historians, with little or no technical background. Most rod makers were self-taught craftsmen whose designs were largely empirical. They had come to tackle making as artisans fully skilled in cabinetry, ornamental millwork, metallurgy, tool-and-die making, lathe operation, and in the fabrication of musical instruments like flutes and violins. Few had any formal background in the mathematics of stress behavior, flexure, and strength of materials, although the lone exception was obviously the remarkable Everett Garrison of New York.

However, the equations found in his notebooks are not earthshaking, although they may seem as impenetrable as hieroglyphics to readers without a modest introduction to the rudiments of engineering math.

Such mathematics are merely the stuff of sophomore courses in mechanics and strength of materials, which lie at the core of engineering curricula throughout the world. But they are primarily focused on the relatively static stresses at play in such conventional structures as buildings and bridges, and offer little insight into the exotic stress behavior of a modern fly rod working its magic on an April afternoon.

Such remarkable performance has its most obvious parallels in aeronautical engineering, in the controlled wing-flexure of aircraft like the Boeing B-47E, and the sophisticated dynamics involved in propeller and helicopter rotor blades.

Phillips was happily at the heart of such technologies, and it is no surprise that he was the first to derive equations that describe the oscillatory performance of a modern fly rod. The Phillips equations were not published in fishing journals of the time, but since I believed his work deserved both a place in history and public attention, they were published when my two-volume *Trout* appeared in 1978.

When the Theodore Gordon Flyfishers scheduled a panel discussion on the exotic new rod materials, at its annual weekend in the late winter of 1974, I was the only panelist who had actually fished the graphite prototypes of Fenwick.

The other panelists were Everett Garrison, Eugene Anderegg and Howard Steere. The first graphite rods introduced by Fenwick proved startlingly stiff and fast, artillery pieces capable of unleashing remarkably long casts with high tip speeds and line velocities, but none yet available had the delicacy to fish the fine tippets necessary on difficult trout streams like the Battenkill, Brodhead, Beaverkill, Ausable, Bois Brule, Firehole, Henry's Fork, Owens, Williamson and Metolius.

Spring creeks like the storied Letort Spring Run in Pennsylvania, the little Kinnikinnik in Wisconsin, the famous Montana spring creeks of the Paradise Valley—on the Nelson and Armstrong and DePuy ranches—Silver Creek in southern Idaho, Hot Creek in eastern California, and the Oregon spring creeks that feed Klamath Lake near Chiloquin, all seemed beyond the promise of the new graphite fly rods. They were powerful and remarkably light, considering their obvious quickness and strength, but they seemed to offer little promise at the delicate end of the fly-fishing spectrum.

I offered that opinion on that wintry day in New York.

Don Phillips was in the audience, and had been experimenting with boron for more than three years, although few had seen his work. His solitary efforts had begun to bear fruit, and the following year, Phillips brought a remarkable prototype to the Theodore Gordon Weekend at the Essex House in New York City. I was sitting at the bar with Charles De Feo and Everett Garrison, enjoying a fine single-malt whiskey, with the wintry twilight of Central Park in its big windows and mahogany-framed mirrors, when Phillips walked in.

"Can you spare fifteen minutes?" He carried a slender aluminum tube six feet in length. "I've got something that might surprise you."

"One-piece rod?" I asked.

"Heard you express some doubts about building really delicate rods with exotic aerospace fibers," Phillips explained. "So I've put together a little surprise."

"Graphite?" I nodded. "Or something else?"

"Boron," he said quietly.

We walked to the darkened ballroom, which stood empty after the last fishing program of the afternoon, and stopped in the aisle between its rows of folding chairs. Glittering chandeliers were high overhead. Phillips drew a frail-looking ebony rod from its six-foot case. Its calibrations were startling, its shaft scarcely the diameter of a soda straw at the cork, and its tip diameter was as delicate as fine pencil lead. Such character was a revelation after the fat fiberglass rods popular after the Second World War.

"It's surprisingly delicate," I said.

"It's an exaggeration intended to make a point," Phillips explained. "I decided to replicate the stiffness characteristics of the Leonard 37L—the six-foot baby Catskill—because you thought it was impossible."

"Can we try casting it a little?"

"Why not?' he smiled. "That's why I brought you in here."

Phillips rummaged through his pockets for a tiny Hardy *Flyweight* fitted with an antique line of British silk. It seemed a bit strange, standing in the dimly lighted ballroom at the Essex House, casting an exotic rod weighing considerably less than an ounce, working the high loop past the chandeliers and delivering soft casts down the faded carpet.

"Well," I confessed, "I've been wrong before."

Like the delicate Leonard 37L itself, the boron *Baby Catskill* was more an elegant little toy than a serious piece of tackle, but the experiment in boron shaped over its permanent boron mandrel had made its intended point. It was obvious that new aerospace materials had the potential, given workable tapers, cutting patterns, mandrels, adhesives, and curing techniques, to produce remarkable lightweight fly rods for the most delicate line weights available. Phillips clearly believed it was possible to build practical rods for line weights more delicate than the WF-3-F lines becoming popular, and still lighter tackle was obviously on the horizon.

His predictions have become a matter of history.

Phillips later provided an eight-foot boron prototype for a trip to the Yellowstone in 1974, and its baptism took place on the cutthroats at Buffalo Ford. It was a remarkable little rod, fitted with a floating DT-4-F line. It was late summer, and the Yellowstone cutthroats were surprisingly picky, sipping cripples from a breakfast spinner fall of tiny *Tricorythodes minutus*. It was a perfect set of conditions to test the light-tackle potential of this eight-foot Phillips prototype, since such diminutive mayflies required size twenty-four hooks, and such hooks required a delicate tippet of 7X. Terry Ross was with me on that summer morning at Buffalo Ford, and we were both impressed with the obvious delicacy of the rod. Neither of us broke off a single fish, although they averaged slightly better than a pound in weight, and the rod also played the fish quite well, its delicate tip cushioning the cobweb tippet against their struggles in the smooth current.

I fished the experimental Phillips again in late September, with the outfitter Frank Meek of Steamboat Springs, whose family tree includes the legendary mountain man and frontier trapper,

Joseph Meek.

We were fishing the Saddle Pocket Ranch on the little Snake. The little river was quite low, and its aspens and big cottonwoods were bright gold. Such conditions also demanded small flies, with *Tricorythodes* spinner swarms each morning, and a palette of tiny *Baetis* mayflies and little slate-colored sedges in the afternoons. Tiny hooks and delicate leaders were the solution, and the boron prototype performed well.

Almost twenty years have passed since those sessions in Wyoming and Colorado, and there is still a unique eight-foot Phillips boron in my collection. It takes a six-weight line, has a spartan grip and skeletal reel seat that echo the ascetic work of Everett Garrison and Paul Young, and unlike most graphite and boron rods, the little Phillips is graced with handsome ferrules of German silver.

It has proved to be a superb piece of equipment.

Phillips subsequently manufactured his boron rods, which were constructed solely of boron filaments over an armature of boron wire, unlike the composite boron-and-graphite rods later manufactured by Rodon. Phillips' firm was called Flycraft Associates, and it manufactured several hundred rods and blanks before production was stopped in 1985.

Most anglers mistakenly assume that carbon graphite rods ultimately came to dominate the fishing world simply because they were better than boron, but knowledgeable anglers who have extensive experience with both materials believe this is nonsense. The history of technology often demonstrates the curious fact, with videotape recorders and computers obvious examples, that superior technology does not inevitably triumph.

Graphite and boron rods are examples.

Carbon graphite fibers are relatively cheap and easily made. They are readily woven into graphite cloth, and were soon adapted to existing methods of tubular rod manufacture. The fabrication methods involved in using fiberglass were virtually the same, although new adhesives and cloth patterns were required. Rod makers found graphite construction methods happily similar to familiar manufacturing technology already in place, and making graphite rods proved less troublesome.

But boron construction proved another matter.

The material itself was not inexpensive, and its filaments are harder than carborundum, which made weaving boron filaments into cloth impossible. Such abrasive filaments would simply abrade and damage each other, whenever they happened to touch, and such fabric would simply fray and fall apart. The widespread mythology that boron was toxic, tended to explode and spray microscopic splinters under stress, and was unusually vulnerable to lightning, had absolutely no basis whatsoever.

Phillips himself confesses that he sometimes waited patiently for days until a minute fragment of boron fiber surfaced from one of his fingers. Such penetrations of his flesh occasionally required minor surgery. But these tiny potshards of boron were not toxic, the rods did not explode, and boron itself is used in electrical insulators.

Such irresponsible gossip may have played a role in the demise of boron, but graphite rods prevailed primarily because they were cheaper and easier to make.

But Phillips was among the pioneers in the revolution that has almost completely eliminated fiberglass rods from the marketplace. Nevertheless, several premier rod makers still work entirely in bamboo, and find themselves hard-pressed to fill their orders. Phillips applied exotic aerospace materials through his research and development at United Technologies, just as the graphite rods developed at Seattle evolved from the aerospace research and development that surrounded the Boeing Company.

No one is better qualified to explore rod technology.

Phillips brings a solid background in basic science and engineering to *The Technology of Fly Rods*. He enjoys the unique perspective of the parallel disciplines involved in propeller blade design and in the intricate mathematics of such performance. He reviews the full spectrum of past rod materials, including the exotic rods of lemonwood and greenheart and snakewood popular among rod makers before the advent of split bamboo. The popularity of cane began with the introduction of *Gigantochloa macrostachya* bamboo, the so-called Calcutta cane that briefly dominated American rod making after the Civil War.

Calcutta was replaced by the lithe *Arundinaria amabilis* of southern China. It is called tea-stick bamboo by experts in the botany of cane, but has been popularly known as Tonkin cane since it caught the eye of nineteenth-century rod makers like William Mitchell.

Tonkin is still the choice of split-cane artisans today.

The Technology of Fly Rods also explores the ill-starred experiments of several manufacturers with tubular rods of aluminum, steel, copper, and beryllium-copper alloys. None of these materials proved workable or popular, like the first rods of fiberglass on balsa wood cores which appeared after the Second World War. But the tubular glass rods that followed proved fishable, were relatively inexpensive, and enjoyed great popularity until boron and carbon fiber rods appeared in 1972.

Phillips also explores the secrets of rod taper and cross section.

Antique wooden rods were planed into round shafts, and the first Calcutta rods were shaped to emulate their appearance, although milling down their corners cost their makers some power fibers. The four-strip rods of William Edwards, the five-strip designs of Robert Crompton, the spiral six-strip designs of Fred Divine, the partially-hollow rods of Lewis Stoner and Edwin Courtney Powell, and the classic six-strip tapers of Charles Murphy and Hiram Lewis Leonard, are compared in terms of their technological virtues and shortcomings. The unique properties of solid construction, tubular rod shafts, and the diameter and wall thickness of such tubular designs, are also explored. Phillips further outlines the basic principles involved in rod performance and design, and the design parameters imposed by the character of a fishery, personal preferences, and the owner's personality. His final chapter explores the process of seeking a new taper and its design specifications.

Don Phillips played a singular role in contemporary rod making, and no one is better qualified to explore the history, materials, technical patents, fittings, behavior and design of fishing rods across the centuries, in his book *The Technology of Fly Rods*.

History tells us that all groundbreaking hypotheses have an inevitable purity of logic, a discipline and character that escapes mere reason, to approach the realm of the poetic. The storied collaboration between James Watson and Francis Crick, working on the molecular structure of DNA in the United Kingdom, is a superb example. Both men rejected a number of theoretical images and structures, before settling on the perfection of their double helix, with its ladder-like struts of hydrogen.

Its beautiful logic ultimately won them the Nobel Prize.

Phillips has discovered a similar potshard of poetry in his microphotographs of tea-stick bamboo, in which each microscopic fiber is hexagonal in shape, a structure unconsciously echoed in the six-strip masterpieces developed by Murphy and Leonard. *The Technology of Fly Rods* explores the science behind the poetry of fly-casting.

Ernest Schwiebert
Princeton, New Jersey
Spring 1999

Chapter 1
INTRODUCTION

The literature of fishing is undoubtedly more abundant than that of any other sport. Although some of its popularity is due to the fact that people started writing about fishing many centuries ago, I suspect that even the current publishing rate of fishing books outpaces any other field. In fact, I'll go out on a limb and conjecture that even the narrower subset of fly-fishing now produces more book titles than other individual sporting pastimes like golf, skiing, hunting, etc. It's not absolutely clear why this is the case. Many other sports take place in the outdoors and immerse the participant into the rich scenery and mysteries of mother nature. Many also require modest degrees of physical coordination, endurance and mental activity. Still others require care and attention to the tools of one's sport, and even opportunities for designing or modifying these tools for better performance and greater pleasure.

I suspect that the allure of fly-fishing is due to all of these reasons. In addition, fly-fishing involves an adversarial relationship where the opponent is attractive, strong (pound for pound) and having a pea-sized brain but impressive instincts for survival. And, unlike hunting, the fly-fishing endgame doesn't necessarily have to result in the prey's death. Of course, all this still doesn't explain why so many books are written about fly-fishing. I like to think that the reason is that the fly-fishing experience is so moving and so rewarding that we are motivated to want to share our knowledge and emotions with others. Well, at least that's my reason for writing this book, and I'm sticking to it!

Not surprisingly, a significant fraction of fly-fishing literature is devoted to various aspects of the fly rod; its history, rod makers, casting techniques, etc. And so, is there really a need for another book on fly rods? Obviously, I think there is such a need. The "technology" of fly rods, or the more technical aspects of their design, construction and performance, has been given very little attention in the modern literature. Actually, just enough has been written to confuse the layman and to whet the appetite of the technically-proficient. And, the content of early literature can be better appreciated when viewed from the perspective of modern science and technology. Do we need to know the technical aspects of fly rods in order to enjoy the sport of fly-fishing? Of course not. No more than we need to tie our own flies (rather than buy them) or to experiment with different leader knots and taper formulae. But, for those of us who want to know more about the sport of fly-fishing, this book is for you. And, who knows, a more practical end result might be that you can cast a little better and/or make better choices when selecting a fly rod for purchase.

By way of background, I have been fishing with flies for about fifty years and intend to keep at it for as long as I am able to do so. My father enjoyed fishing, but my grandfather was a dyed-in-the-wool fly-fisher who owned several exquisite bamboo fly rods. As I remember, I wasn't allowed to even touch these rods, never mind fish or cast with them. Nevertheless, I did get a telescoping steel fly rod outfit one Christmas when I was a kid. I vaguely remember a few years of frustration, during which time I satisfied my urge to catch trout by using it with worms on our local streams in Springfield, Massachusetts. I vividly remember my first fly-caught trout on that rod, however. At age 15, three of us were fishing the South Branch, a nice, remote little stream which is probably encased in concrete today. We had spent a few hours worm fishing with some success and we were out of bait, standing on a little bridge spanning the stream. As we were looking down at the water, I noticed a subtle dimple in the water's surface near a bush at stream side. On a lark, I tied on some non-descript fly and sort of threw it (it would be a major exaggeration to claim that I cast it) in the general direction of that dimpled rise. Miraculously, a foot-long trout came out from under the bush and grabbed the fly, hooking himself while my friends and I froze in disbelief. I remember landing that trout by yanking him up and onto the bridge, but what I remember most was seeing him during the split second before he inhaled the fly, while he was charging from his hiding place. From that point on, I was hooked for life!

After getting my degree in mechanical engineering, I went to work in Connecticut for one of the country's largest aerospace manufacturers. During the 34 years that I worked for this company I was able to afford appropriate fly-fishing and fly tying equipment and enough trips around the country to both broaden my fly-fishing experience and satisfy my urge to visit new places. Most important, however, during that time I had access to some of the country's top engineers and scientists. Anytime I had a technical question on fly rod materials, aerodynamics, structures, etc., the answer was only a short walk or a phone call away. This proximity to technical expertise was essential during the 1970-1985 time period, when I undertook the after-hours development of the world's first boron fly rod.

My employer was one of three organizations who were in the forefront of development of boron fibers for aerospace applications in the 1960s and 1970s. Our research laboratory was developing the fiber for sale to others, while several other company divisions were using boron fibers in aerospace component hardware. Fortunately, I was intimately involved in both the fiber production process and the prototype hardware development effort. During the same period we were also very much involved in graphite fiber research and hardware development, giving me a unique insight into the current state-of-the-art, limitations and outlook for two different, competitive material systems.

From the very beginning, it was apparent to me that boron and graphite fibers had considerable potential for fly rods. My main challenges were to develop a valid method for distributing the high performance boron fibers into useful fly rod tapers and to develop a compatible manufacturing approach which was practical and not too costly. Fortunately, the periodic availability of scrap materials plus the patience of an understanding management permitted me to pursue these challenges while still holding down a full-time job. Although my primary focus was on boron fly rods, much effort was spent also experimenting with graphite, cane and fiberglass, in order to gain a full appreciation of these contemporary materials. Eventually, I solved the more fundamental design and manufacturing problems and went on to form my own company, Flycraft Associates, which manufactured and sold several hundred boron fly rods and blanks to fly-fishers around the world. Flycraft Associates closed its doors in 1985, primarily since boron fibers remained a very expensive material without much hope of competing with the rapidly developing graphite fly rod technology. The knowledge gained during the period of 1970-1985, plus seasoning of the past 14 years has provided the basis for this book.

The following pages will give the reader a perspective of how fly rod technology has evolved since the earliest Chinese and Egyptian fishermen fed their families more than two thousand years before the birth of Christ. This will include a summary of where the technology stands today and the outlook for the future. The trail of U.S. patents granted since the mid-nineteenth century will also be reviewed, to round out the historical aspects of fly rod technology. Then we'll review the processes used in fly rod manufacturing and tackle the broad subject of fly-rod design, with special emphasis on rod functions, material properties, length/configuration alternatives, blank spine and various design approaches. Rod components will also be briefly discussed, to the extent that they can materially affect the performance or endurance of the fly rod. Finally, we'll take an in-depth look at the fly rod's behavior and function during casting, perhaps giving you some insights that might help improve your casting.

Although a primary objective of this material is to inform the reader on many of the technical aspects of fly rods, every attempt will be made to minimize the use of technical jargon. When technical terms must be used, I'll try to explain them in everyday language. On the other hand, for those few engineering concepts and equations that will be presented, all symbols and units will be defined, to satisfy the inevitable questions from those with technical backgrounds. When of necessity I'm obliged to drift into such esoteric detail, I trust that the rest of you will bear with me and move on to the next paragraph.

As the various technical issues of fly rods are discussed herein, there will be instances where there is less than unanimous agreement in the fly-fishing community. In such instances I'll try to fairly present both sides of the story, but I won't hesitate to state my personal views. If you catch me making a pedantic statement on some bit of engineering trivia, you can be assured that the concept or relationship is rather fundamental and widely accepted in engineering circles. The content of this book has been based on the review of hundreds of books and magazine articles and dozens of interviews of fly rod experts. Wherever practical, the unique contributions of others will be attributed to them via direct references. In addition, I have included many bibliographies in the appendices to this book, to assist others who may wish to travel down this same road and enjoy further the rich technical history of fly rods.

Chapter 2
THE HISTORY OF FLY ROD TECHNOLOGY

Nowadays it would take only a few minutes in a library or on the Internet to determine who invented the laser, the diesel engine or the phonograph and to ascertain when those devices were invented. But, how about some inventions a great deal older like the fulcrum/lever system or the wheel? We now have a dilemma in that these fundamental breakthroughs were invented well before the existence of any organized body of journalism or record-keeping. We are thus forced to only approximate when these inventions took place, from ancient paintings and engravings. The same situation exists with our favorite subject of fishing rods. We know from old artwork that the fishing rod was in use thousands of years ago, and yet we haven't a clue as to who, when or where this event first took place. Nevertheless, let's not let this lack of knowledge be overly inhibiting. Let's use our imagination to tentatively reconstruct the earliest days of fishing, so as to give this chapter a starting point.

The Beginnings

According to Ernest Schwiebert (Table A-3, No. 17) the earliest likely fishers were the Chinese or the Egyptians, based on evidence dated about 2000 B.C. It's not too difficult to imagine fishermen on the banks of the Nile or the Yangtze, using baited hooks with hand lines but wishing that they could somehow throw that baited hook a little further out into the river. They might have eventually

*Assyrian wall relief – Nineveh, 1000 B.C.
From Ernest Schwiebert's* Trout.

caught sight of nearby reeds, canes or saplings and deduced that they could indeed swing the bait well out into the current by tying the line onto the end of their newly acquired fishing rod. And, after confirming the success of this rig, they would certainly notice that fewer big fish were broken off due to the shock-absorbing quality of the relatively flexible rod tip. Perhaps that's how the first fishing rod was created. A.J. McClane (Table A-3, No. 10) tells us that the Shang Dynasty Chinese constructed very strong poles for carrying water by splitting bamboo into segments and then lashing the segments together very tightly. It seems logical to conclude that they would have eventually transferred this "technology" to their fishing rods.

Egyptian tomb mural at Beni Hasan, 2000 B.C. From Ernest Schwiebert's Trout.

Schwiebert also describes one of the first documented references to fly-fishing, a manuscript by a Macedonian named Aelianus dated about 300 A.D. Aelianus described a rod about 6 feet long, with an attached line of equal length and a feathered hook. We can only guess from what material the rod was made.

Casting the Fly

In all probability, the first flies were dapped on the water, using the rod as a convenient extension of the arm to place the feathered hook at the right spot. There appears to be no documentary evidence marking the beginnings of fly-casting, but here again we can perhaps use our imagination to draft a believable scenario. The extremely low weight of a fly must have concerned earlier fly-fishers as they attempted to place their flies on the water, especially in any sort of a wind. A most logical solution to that problem would be to add some kind of weight to the line, to help propel the fly to its intended location. Of course, we know how herky-jerky such weights behave when flipped by the tip of a rod. Accordingly, some rather bright early fly-fisher must have conceived the idea of distributing this weight by using a relatively heavy line attached to the rod tip. And, as he became proficient at casting the line, he might have noticed that it had the tendency to pull the rod away from him. This could have suggested to him that he could achieve greater "casting" distances if he fed additional line loosely through a loop on the rod tip, as the cast line's energy sought to pull the fly to greater distances. This would logically lead to a series of guides on the rod to help feed the line to the tip-top and to some sort of "winch" or reel to store additional line. Perhaps that's how fly-casting got started, during the first thousand years or so after the birth of Christ.

Precisely where and when this casting first occurred may never be known, but we can at least begin to estimate the time period from currently available literature. Figure 2-1 (on the following page) shows a time line for fishing rod technology through six centuries. This figure depicts some of the rod materials that were introduced and the authors whose books contained useful information on the history of fishing rod technology. It is both interesting and perplexing that the 18th century has relatively few significant literature contributions. A more complete bibliography is included in Appendix A. Note that most of the early writings were by British authors. This does not necessarily mean that notable developments weren't taking place elsewhere in the world; it's just that we haven't yet found many documents which have chronicled such work.

Edward Fitzgibbon (aka Ephemera) describes casting of the line in considerable detail in his *Handbook of Angling*, 1847 (Table A-2, No. 2), so it is clear that fly-casting as we know it existed early in the 1800s. Actually, the earliest reference on casting the line that I could find was in Thomas Best's *Art of Angling*, 1787 (Table A-1, No. 15). His description of casting in Chapter V, however, perhaps raises more questions than it answers. Per Best, "When you throw your line, wave the rod in a small circumference round your head, and never make a return of it before it has had its full scope; for if you do the fly will snap off." This suggests a questionable technique, but recognizes the timeless need to delay the casting stroke until the line has reached its greatest extension. Since neither Berners nor Walton/Cotton (Table A-1, Nos. 1 and 11) mention the concept of casting, it would seem likely that the origins of this art began in the 1700s. Whenever it did occur, this marked the beginning of the development of the fly rod and its materials and tapers. At this point in time, fly rod technology probably began to branch off from general fishing rod technology, because of the unique requirements imposed by fly-casting.

From Berners' Treatyse of Fysshynge Wyth an Angle.

FIGURE 2-1
Fishing Rod Technology Time Line

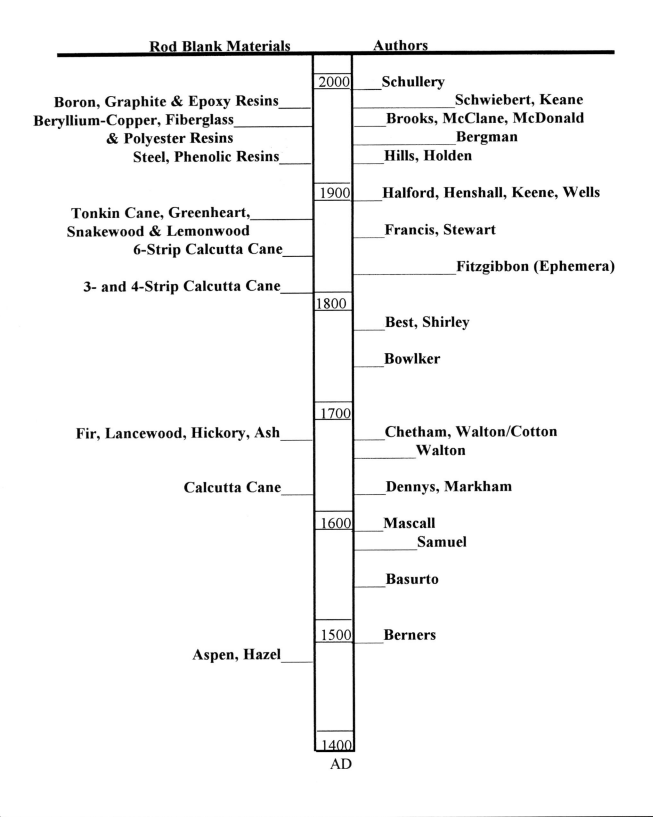

Rod Blank Materials   **Authors**

2000 — Schullery

Boron, Graphite & Epoxy Resins___   Schwiebert, Keane
Beryllium-Copper, Fiberglass_____   Brooks, McClane, McDonald
& Polyester Resins   Bergman
Steel, Phenolic Resins___   Hills, Holden

1900 — Halford, Henshall, Keene, Wells

Tonkin Cane, Greenheart,___
Snakewood & Lemonwood   Francis, Stewart
6-Strip Calcutta Cane___
                                                                        Fitzgibbon (Ephemera)
3- and 4-Strip Calcutta Cane___

1800
          Best, Shirley

          Bowlker

1700
Fir, Lancewood, Hickory, Ash___   Chetham, Walton/Cotton
                                                                Walton

Calcutta Cane___   Dennys, Markham

1600 — Mascall
                                                Samuel

          Basurto

1500 — Berners

Aspen, Hazel___

1400
AD

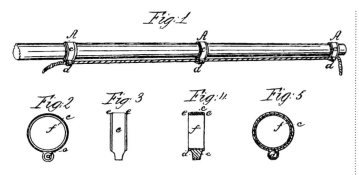

H. Pritchard's Line Guide Patent No. 25,693.

Early Materials in England

Although reeds and canes are mentioned in earlier manuscripts, Berners seems to be the first to document the use of wood for fly rods in the 15th century. Hazel was particularly popular well into the 17th century, and was endorsed by Dennys in his lengthy poem, "Secrets of Angling," 1613 (Table A-1, No. 5). Whichever material was used, it needed to be tapered in order to both remove unnecessary weight and to achieve the flexibility needed in the tip area for casting and fish fighting. Although the first wooden fly rods were probably whittled or planed by hand, mechanization eventually permitted tapered milling and doweling.

Calcutta cane began to gain favor in the 1600s, especially for butt sections. Rod makers and fly-fishers were undoubtedly beginning to tire of casting these 12- to 20-foot rods, and were certainly always searching for new materials which would

be lighter and yet stiff and strong enough to survive the strains of casting and fish fighting. The introduction of fir, lancewood, hickory and ash in the late 1600s gave the rod makers more wood choices, but over the next two centuries increasing international trade gave them opportunities to experiment with many more varieties of wood. Figure 2-2 (below) lists all of the natural materials used for fly rods which I could find during my research for this book. Figure 2-3 (following page) tabulates the latin designation and geographic source for some of the more common ones.

Drawing of a kneeling caster by Louis Rhead, from "The Speckled Brook Trout."

While working with Calcutta cane, rod makers began to appreciate that most of the stiffness and strength were found in the outer fibers of the culm;

FIGURE 2-2
Natural Fishing Rod Materials

Ash	Crabtree	Japanese Cane	Medlar	Tonkin Cane
Barberry	Dagama	Jucara Prieto	Osage Orange	Walnut
Basswood	Fir	Juniper	Paddlewood	Whalebone
Beefwood	Greenheart	Kranji	Pingow	Willow
Bethabara(Washaba)	Hazel	Lancewood	Purpleheart	Yew
Blackthorn	Hickory	Lemonwood	Pyengadu	
Calcutta Cane	Hornbeam	Logwood	Shadblow	
Cedar	Ironback	Mahoe	Snakewood	
Chow	Ironwood	Maple	Thornwood	

FIGURE 2-3
Common Natural Rod Materials

Material	Latin Name	Geographic Source
Ash (White)	*Fraxinus americana*	Eastern USA
Calcutta Cane	*Gigantichloa macrostachya*	India, Burma, Thailand, Malaysia
Greenheart	*Nectandra rodeoi*	Guyana
Hickory (Shagbark)	*Carya ovata*	Eastern USA
Lancewood	*Oxanda laneolata*	Guyana
Lemonwood	*Pittisporum eugenioides*	New Zealand
Snakewood	*Moraceae piratinera*	N.E. South America
Tonkin Cane	*Arundinaria amabilis*	Kwangtung, China

actually in the outer quarter of an inch or less. In the early 1800s, rod makers split the hollow culm into very narrow strips (called splines), removing most of the useless pith from these strips, and combining these strips into various geometries and configurations. The tapering and joining of numbers of individual strips of Calcutta cane became a skilled art. At first, these multi-strip pieces were used exclusively for rod tips, but eventually they were also incorporated into butt sections.

During the 1800s and well into the early 1900s rod makers increasingly understood that the lightest, and therefore the best cane fly rod construction positioned the outer cane fibers at the outside of the rod surface. As further explained in Chapter 6, this provides the greatest stiffness with the least amount of weight. Literally a century of experimentation accrued with rod makers trying 2, 3, 4, 5, 6, 7, 8, and even up to 12 strips of cane. Cross-sections of these designs ranged all the way from triangular through circular, the latter obtained by increasing the number of strips and planing or sanding off the corners. All during this experimentation there were hundreds of pages written on which shape was best and the reasons therefor. Please refer to Chapter 7 for more information on this subject. In essence, though, the selection of the best cross-sectional shape has to be a thoughtful compromise of stiffness, weight, structural integrity and manufacturing cost. Over the test of time, the 6-strip construction has come out the winner in this cane construction debate.

America's Cane Rod Revolution

Until the mid-1800s essentially all of the fly rod's technology advances were made in England. According to A.J. McClane (Table A-3, No. 10), this all changed in 1846, when a clever gunsmith, Samuel Phillippe of Easton Pennsylvania built the first rod tip from 6 strips of Calcutta cane. The rod butt was probably made from ash. Although the historians are not unanimous about this, it appears as though Samuel Phillippe's son, Solon, actually built the first six-strip rod in 1859 which was made entirely of Calcutta cane. Neither Samuel nor Solon made any significant numbers of fly rods, and according to Martin J. Keane (Table A-3 No. 15), it was the later efforts of Ebenezer Green, Charles Murphy and William Mitchell which set the standards for a highly functional and attractive fly rod.

Despite the significant accomplishments of the Phillippes, Green, Murphy and Mitchell, it was Hiram L. Leonard who truly put the cane fly rod on the map by establishing a system of design and manufacturing methods and machinery which placed the cane fly rod within the affordable reach of larger numbers of fly-fishers. Leonard built his first rods in 1871 of ash and lancewood, but he first offered all split-cane rods in 1874. Leonard's legacy, passed on to his associates Ed Payne, Fred

Thomas, Eustis Edwards, Gene Edwards, Bill Edwards, Fred Divine, Hiram Hawes, Loman Hawes, Thomas Chubb and George Varney still lives with us today in the fly rods of Orvis, Winston, Thomas & Thomas, Powell and dozens of one-man shops across the country.

Although the Calcutta-type of cane was dominant for nearly three centuries, Tonkin cane gradually replaced it, starting in the late 1890s. By 1910 most of the high-quality cane rods were made from Tonkin cane (also called tea-stick bamboo) because of its equivalent mechanical properties and much-improved straightness and appearance. Raw Calcutta cane culms were notoriously crooked and had to be manually scorched and straightened for acceptance by the fly rod market. By comparison, the Tonkin cane from the Kwangtung province of China grew up to 40-80 feet tall, and straight enough to not require any pre-market flaming or bending. Although World War II caused an interruption in the availability of Tonkin cane, this "crop" of fly rod raw material remains accessible today at varying degrees of dependability.

Even though the hexagonal, six-strip version represents today's standard of excellence for Tonkin cane fly rods, some other very interesting cane designs have been produced over the years. Here's a few of these other configurations, each of which had devotees and followers at various times:

- The double-built (one cane rod inside another), nine-sided and steel-reinforced designs of Hardy
- The 4-sided designs of Bill Edwards (brother of Gene), Ebenezer Green and Sam Carlson.
- The 5-strip designs of Robert Crompton and Nat Uslan
- Fred Divine's eight-sided rods
- Fred Divine's and Letcher Lambuth's spiraling-strip rods
- The hollow, fluted and scalloped interior designs of E.C. Powell and Lew Stoner

Many of these variations would not have been achievable with the animal hide glues generally available to the earliest rod makers. In fact, many of the intermediate (between guides) thread wrappings found on earlier rods were added primarily as an added assurance against rod failure due to spline separation. Over the years, the development of synthetic glues has provided a tenacious bond between cane strips which remains strong even in the presence of moisture. Improved varnishes have also helped to inhibit moisture penetration, at film thicknesses which don't add too much weight to

the fly rod. The Orvis development of phenolic resin impregnation in the 1940s was another innovation which helped to maintain the structural integrity of cane rods in the presence of moisture, although at a discernible weight penalty. Some cane-rod makers used flaming or baking to cosmetically darken the outer appearance of the rod's surface. In doing so, they learned that heat also hardened the cane's fibers and natural resins, stiffening the rod to a slight degree at no increase in weight. Although heating increased brittleness somewhat, this technique provided rod makers with yet another tool for fly rod design and manufacture.

One of the continuing dilemmas for cane-rod makers has been to minimize the effect of the culm's many nodes when building fly rods. These nodes or rings are present in the parent culm along every twelve inches or so of its length and, of course, segments of the culm's nodes are also present in all of the several strips making up the fly rod. The nodes are discontinuities in the outer fibers of the culm and are neither as strong nor as stiff as the fibers. Over the years, rod makers have filed the nodes down so that they don't protrude above the otherwise continuous culm surface on either side, leaving an aesthetically better product. They have also tried many different patterns for staggering the nodes among the several cane splines, so that the weaker node areas are not located at the same place in the final end product. There seems to have been no single pattern which has proven to be the best, and many different approaches have been used with success.

One ingenious solution to the node problem is to cut out the nodes altogether and to splice together the short rod splines before assembly into a rod blank section. Although expensive because of the time and precision required, this approach proved to be quite successful and barely noticeable in the final product. By cutting the ends of the splines at a very shallow angle, sufficient gluing area is obtained to form a very high strength splice. This technique probably evolved out of the early common practice of joining multi-section wooden fly rods with shallow-angle splices. With proper orientation of the splice surface relative to

An early fly rod splice, from Paul Schullery's American Fly Fishing.

the plane of rod bending, these spliced wooden rods were very successful. Even without the use of glue, the tightly wrapped helical binding kept the sections together until the binding was removed.

Metal Fly Rods

By the start of the 20th century, rod-making skills were quite advanced and well-made Tonkin cane fly rods were beginning to cost more than some would-be fly-fishers could afford. To fill this market void, new rod materials were developed and introduced, none of which survived the long-term test of time. The Horton Manufacturing Company first introduced solid steel fly rods in 1913, according to McClane (Reference Table A-3, No. 10). These fly rods were very heavy and flexible and found few satisfied customers. Several manufacturers however soon introduced hollow steel rods which were still fairly heavy, but were both usable and affordable. Lightweight aluminum alloy fly rods were developed, but did not gain acceptance because they could not withstand the high stresses of casting and fish-fighting without exceeding the alloy's maximum yield strength. Copper fly rods also met the same fate, for the same reason plus their excessive weight. Beryllium-copper fly rods enjoyed a brief popularity since they weren't prone to rusting like their steel counterparts, but they were still top-heavy compared to a good cane rod.

The Introduction of Fiberglass

Although hollow steel rods were fairly popular for decades, their dominance of the low-cost market ended during the 1940s with the introduction of fiberglass. Victor Johnson and Victor Johnson Jr, have documented the history of fiberglass rod development in considerable detail (Table A-3, No. 25). Schwiebert (Table A-3, No. 17) also chronicles the history of fiberglass fly rods in some detail, starting with some of the rudimentary experiments of E.R. Hewitt just before World War II. Hewitt attempted to simulate the structure of cane by laying nylon fibers over a tapered, fine wooden dowel, embedding the fibers in a plastic resin. This experiment failed because the nylon fibers were not stiff enough to withstand the stresses of a working fly rod.

The first fishing rods made from fiberglass were developed in the mid 1940s by Robert Gayle and a Mr. McGuire, both from Missouri. It is not clear whether they worked independently or collaboratively, but the process involved continuous casting where resin-saturated fiberglass yarn was formed into a slender square rod, cut to the desired length and then ground to the desired taper of circular cross-section. These fishing rods, first offered by the Phantom and Shakespeare companies, were not very well-received by the fly-fishing community because they were still quite heavy, but they were and still are favored for rough-and-tumble fishing rod applications where casting is not an important factor.

Also in 1946, Dr. Arthur Howald replicated Hewitt's experiments using a balsa wood core, phenolic resins and the then newly-available fiberglass fibers. These experiments were so successful that Shakespeare licensed the Howald concepts and produced fishing rods of this configuration up until the early 1950s. By then they had developed another less expensive approach, using a removable steel mandrel, resin-saturated yarns of fiberglass and fully automated machinery. They continue to use this approach today for everything from fishing rods to antenna masts.

Also during the same time period, a Dr. Glenn G. Havens, working with the Convair Company (an aircraft manufacturer), was developing a competitive process using a resin-saturated fiberglass cloth which was tightly wrapped over a removable steel mandrel. This process, and its many variations, has formed the basis for the manufacture of most fiberglass and graphite fly rods over the past 50 years. In the late 1940s and early 1950s, these fly rods were developed without much design sophistication. Most of the attention was directed toward keeping costs down and some of the early fiberglass fly rods were very poor casting instruments. Nevertheless, with the leadership of technically proficient people like Russ Peak, Harry Wilson, Arthur Neuman, Ferdinand Claudio, Vince Cummings, Gary Loomis, Jim Green, Don Green, Jon Tarantino and others, fiberglass fly rods finally reached their expected potential and by the early 1970s captured a sizeable portion of the fly rod market.

In addition to the early problems with taper design, early fiberglass fly rods also had a propensity to soften with age, losing some of its original stiffness. This was largely due to moisture intrusion into the composite fiberglass/resin material, where it gradually destroyed the chemical bond between the fibers and the polyester resin. Subsequent development of silane fiber coatings succeeded in maintaining bond integrity even in the presence of moisture. Also, the eventual availability of epoxy resins provided further retention of resin bonding properties under conditions of adsorbed moisture. Another significant development that improved fiberglass fly rods was the introduction of S-glass, a fiber whose stiffness or modulus of elasticity is significantly higher than that of the E-glass fibers previously in use. Although S-glass had been used since the 1960s in such high-tech aerospace applications as aircraft propeller blades, it wasn't until the 1970s that S-glass was successfully used for fly rods. And so, fly rod technology continued to march on, with perhaps the best yet to come. These were significant accomplishments since, for the first time, man-made materials were used to construct high-performance fly rods.

Boron and Graphite Fibers

During the decade of the 1960s, several government agencies of the United States and the United Kingdom invested considerable research and development into advanced, high-performance fibers, especially boron and graphite (carbon). These investments were readily justified because of the large improvements predicted in materials strength, stiffness and weight. Initially, boron received the most attention, but soon graphite also was funded heavily because of the greater potential for lower cost. These improvements have since been proven in aircraft that can fly farther, faster and with larger payloads, plus thousands of other high-tech applications where weight, stiffness or aerodynamic profile is critical. Fortunately, many consumer applications benefit from the same criteria, including golf clubs, tennis racquets, etc. It was thus inevitable that fishing rod manufacturers would begin experimenting with boron and graphite in the late 1960s. The promise of lighter rods and longer casts was too tantalizing to ignore.

In late 1971, a middle-aged aerospace engineer by the name of Don Phillips (that's right, that's me) started experimenting with fly rods made from boron fibers and epoxy resins. This was quite a natural shift in my life because I was a life-long fly-fisher and my employer, United Technologies Corporation, was one of the first to produce boron fibers in the research laboratory. In fact, while I was experimenting evenings with boron fly rods in my home workshop I was also working during the day to find consumer applications for boron fibers and to help grow the fiber manufacturing process from a research endeavor to a viable commercial production venture. The periodic availability of scrap materials and the ready access to some of the country's top scientists and engineers made my moonlighting effort a very practical endeavor. In the beginning, I followed the lead of Hewitt and Howald, laying fine strips of boron fiber/epoxy resin tape onto very delicate permanent mandrels of balsa wood. Using this configuration, I caught my first trout on a boron fly rod in April of 1972.

The fragility of the balsa core soon doomed this approach and I turned my attention to solid boron/epoxy fly rods, using various wire materials as permanent mandrels. In 1973 I also incorporated an additional outer layer of graphite/epoxy on my fly rods, to improve the rod's outward appearance and to somewhat soften the inherently stiff and brittle nature of boron. By 1977 however, after incorporating many manufacturing process improvements, I was able to return to an all-boron/epoxy construction which worked very well for trouting applications. In 1985, I closed my small one-man business, after producing over 700 fly rods under the label of Flycraft Associates. By that time, graphite fiber costs had lowered to the point where boron fibers were uncompetitive. In addition, graphite fiber improvements and rod industry developments had all but eliminated the performance advantages initially enjoyed by my boron fly rods in the early 1970s. Many rod companies worked with and sold various types of boron fly rods, but current activity is limited to specialty reinforcement uses where the unique properties of boron fibers are worth its relatively high cost.

In 1973, Fenwick was the first manufacturer to offer graphite fly rods for sale. Many other companies soon followed suit and the race for market share was in full swing by the late 1970s. Unfortunately, many of these initial offerings were premature; breakage rates were high and although these rods could cast a country mile, they were lacking in presentation delicacy and general fishability. Now, 20 years later, the industry is awash with high-quality fly rods of all types. Today, any fly-fisher who can't find a graphite fly rod well suited to his personal casting and fishing needs either isn't looking very hard or is beyond salvation.

Graphite's material properties have improved significantly since the 1970s and, perhaps more important, the rod companies have learned how to take advantage of the unique characteristics of all the various constituents of advanced composite materials. Although twenty-five years of development might seem to be a rather long period of time for graphite fly rods to mature to their current state of development, this isn't unreasonable in view of the rod companies' limited technical staffing and truly significant technological challenges. Some of the more significant challenges were:

- working with a continually changing family of graphite fibers and epoxy resins, with accompanying varying physical, chemical and mechanical properties
- changing fiber orientation to provide the lightest fly rod, with satisfactory structural integrity
- using multiple fiber types, to reduce costs or decrease weight, while dealing with the problems inherent in fiber mixing
- developing lightweight ferrules, without either hurting the continuity of rod flex nor introducing areas of high stress concentration
- wrestling with the at-times contradictory requirements of fly rod weight, cost/price, and marketable customer warrantees

Chapters 4 and 7 have more detail on these technical issues.

Ferrules and Other Components

The need to assemble and disassemble fly rods has always been an important design consideration, especially the early rods which were four to six yards long and whose weight was measured in pounds rather than ounces. When the fly-fisher lived near his or her favorite stream, which was often the case, carrying such a formidable device when assembled would have been quite difficult. And, traveling any real distances by way of horse,

Some early ferrules.

carriage or whatever would seem to have presented insurmountable challenges. The use of multiple sections was also often dictated by the difficulty in making relatively long rod sections in one continuous piece. The need to change materials at various stages along the rod's length also necessitated the use of some type of joint. Spliced joints were first used, and they were sometimes left assembled until the season's end, because of the time required

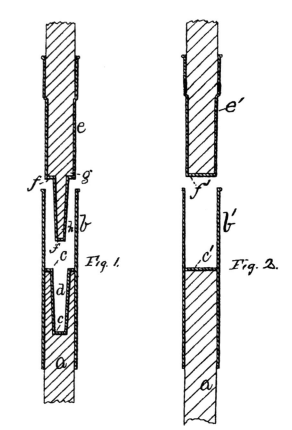

H.L. Leonard's Waterproof Ferrule Patent No. 169,181.

for assembly and disassembly.

True convenience with regard to rod joint assembly and disassembly wasn't available until metallic ferrules were developed. Some of the first ferrules were cone-shaped brass spikes which mated with a female receptacle internal to an adjacent rod section. Separation during fishing was usually prevented by either pinning the two ferrule halves together or by employing some sort of internal or external latching mechanism. Many of the early constant-diameter ferrules consisted simply of brass or bronze tubes;

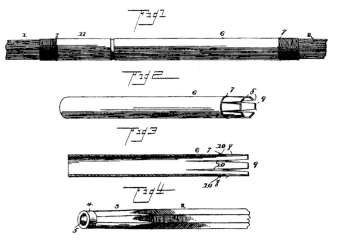

Varney's Serrated Ferrule Patent No. 422,470.

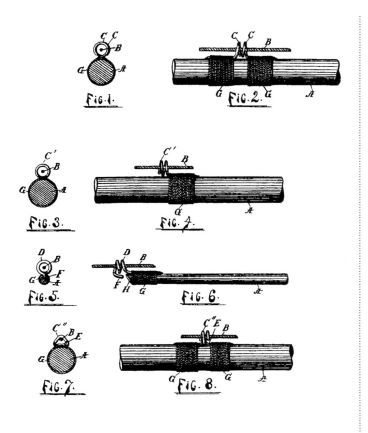

J.C. Parker's Line Guide Patent No. 396,707.

with one end permanently fixed to one rod section and the other end acting as a receptacle for the other rod section. When precision machining or drawing became available, two-piece ferrules were developed whose mating surfaces had enough friction to keep the rod sections together during use. Designs based on this premise still dominate the quality cane rods being made today. For over two centuries, metallic ferrules were constructed from brass, bronze, aluminum, steel, and nickel-silver. Today, nickel-silver is the standard for high-quality cane fly rod ferrules because of its excellent appearance, compatible physical properties and self-lubricity.

When fiberglass and then graphite fly rods were initially developed, the rod companies developed ferrules made from these same materials. This development continues today. Keane (Table A-3, No 15) and Schwiebert (Table A-3, No. 17) have chronicled a massive amount of data on the history of ferrules, line guides, reel seats and handles. I have largely relied on these sources for preparing Figure 2-4, a technology time line for fly rod components. Jon Tarantino and Jim Green were instrumental in developing the spigot and feralite ferrules, respectively, in the late 1950s. Note that technical improvements continue today, although not at the frenetic pace of a century earlier.

Group of early guides.

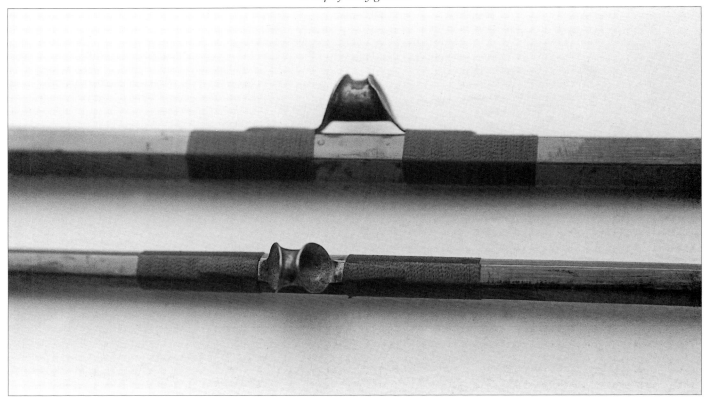

FIGURE 2-4
Rod Component Technology Timeline

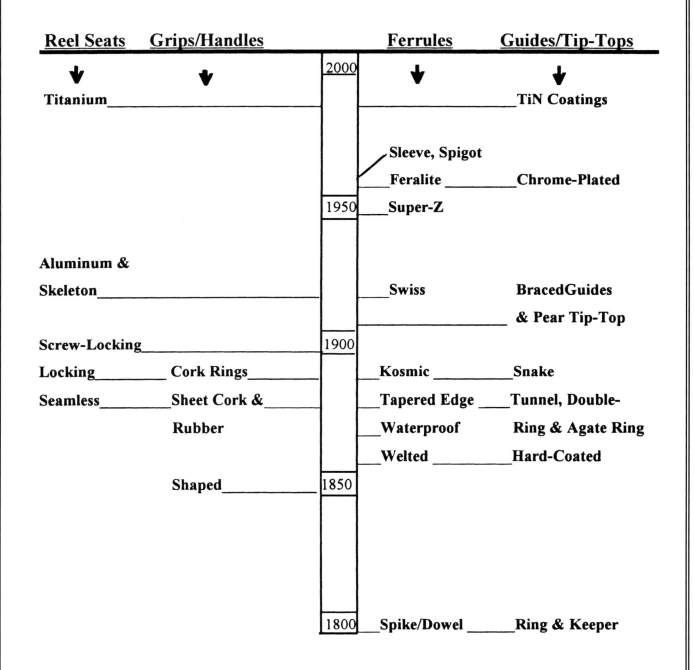

Reel Seats	Grips/Handles		Ferrules	Guides/Tip-Tops
↓	↓	**2000**	↓	↓
Titanium				TiN Coatings
			Sleeve, Spigot	
			Feralite	Chrome-Plated
		1950	Super-Z	
Aluminum &				
Skeleton			Swiss	BracedGuides
				& Pear Tip-Top
Screw-Locking		**1900**		
Locking	Cork Rings		Kosmic	Snake
Seamless	Sheet Cork &		Tapered Edge	Tunnel, Double-
	Rubber		Waterproof	Ring & Agate Ring
			Welted	Hard-Coated
	Shaped	**1850**		
		1800	Spike/Dowel	Ring & Keeper

Chapter 3
U.S. FISHING ROD PATENTS

Background

Patent activity is an excellent measure of the level of creativity and technical effort ongoing in a particular field. For that reason I allocated some of my research for this book toward the patent activity in fishing rods. My attention was not limited to fly rods, since the differences between rods for fly-fishing, bait casting, spinning, etc. are not too significant with regard to patentable features. The purpose of this investigation was to determine how the level and nature of patent activity has varied over the years. Because of the sheer number of patents involved, no attempt could be made to evaluate their relative importance.

The United States patent system was enacted by law in 1790, to encourage creative thinking and foster business expansion through innovation. The system grants a monopoly to the inventor for an initial period (currently 17 years) and the issuance of a patent publicizes the invention, thereby increasing the potential for spawning additional ideas. An invention is patentable if it is a truly new idea, providing an improved solution to a real problem, and if its feasibility is demonstrated by some extent of reduction to practice. A rather rigorous process is followed to verify that these requirements are met.

Information Sources

The patent information gathered for this chapter was gathered from several sources. An excellent resource book, *U.S. Fishing Rod Patents and Other Tackle*, 1990, (Table A-3, No. 23) by Mary Kefover Kelly lists all fishing rod patents issued between April 18, 1854 and December 31, 1931. These patents were all classified by the US Patent Office as being in Class 43 (Fishing, Trapping and Vermin Destroying), Sub-Classes 18 through 26. Ms. Kelly's list was further reduced to eliminate all patents relating to flies, reels, accessories and attachments. I further organized the list so each patent fell into one of the following six categories:

Fishing Rods and Blanks
Rod/Reel Combos
Ferrules, Joints and Splices
Handles, Grips and Butts
Reel Seats
Guides and Tip-Tops

There may have been some fishing rod patents issued between 1790 and 1854, but a disastrous fire at the US Patent Office destroyed any evidence of same. Another source for this project came from our new friend, the Internet. An electronic data base now exists at the Patent Office, covering patents issued from January 1976 to the present. I was able to access this data base thanks to a patent attorney friend in Connecticut. The remaining patents, those issued from 1932 through 1975, were located the hard way, by many hours of research at the State Library in Hartford, Connecticut and at the US Patent Office in Washington, DC. On completing this effort, I had identified a total of 1101 US fishing rod patents issued in the 145-year period between 1854 and 1998. These patents comprised the following categories; fishing rods and blanks, 329; rod/reel combos, 165; ferrules/joints/splices, 68; handles/grips/butts, 199; guides/tip-tops, 167; and reel seats, 173. I was frankly surprised at the significant number of patents on handles/grips/butts, guides/tip-tops and reel seats.

Chubb's Tip-Top Patent No. 277,230.

Summary of U.S. Fishing Rod Patents

The patent data is summarized on Figure 3-1, which is a histogram depicting the number of patents issued during each decade for the rod/blank category and for all other categories of fishing rod patents, through 1998. Analysis of this illustration plus the supporting detail data, leads one to the following observations.

Overall, U.S. fishing rod patent activity has increased from near-zero in the 1850s to almost 160 patents one hundred years later in the decade of the 1950s. Currently, patent activity (1990s) has dropped to nearly half of the 1950s level. The reasons for this are not obvious, but it may have something to do with the rapid rate of current technological change and the resulting lesser importance of a 17-year monopoly.

Note that Figure 3-1 has four distinct spikes of increased activity in the 1880s, the 1900s, the 1930s and the 1950s. The 1880s increase is probably due to the introduction of Tonkin cane in that period and the considerable energies of rod makers like Leonard, and his contemporaries. The reason for the 1900s increase is unknown, but perhaps it could have been due to the prior publishing of important books by such key authors as Halford, Henshall, Keene and Wells. The increases in the 1930s and the 1950s seem irrevocably associated with the introduction of metal and then fiberglass rods during those decades. Even though there's usually a delay of about two years from invention conception until patent issuance, the timing of all of these events seems consistent with one another.

About 30% of all patents relate to the overall rod and/or blank. By contrast a mere 6% relate to ferrules, joints and splices. The remainder are fairly evenly divided (15-18% each) between rod/reel combos, handles/grips/butts, guides/tip-tops and reel seats. It seems hard to believe that there are 173 patentable ways to attach a reel to a fishing rod. Or 167 patentable inventions related to line guides and tip-tops.

Patenting of rod/reel combinations had some flurries of activity in the 1900s and the 1950s, relative to their level of other decades. Similarly, reel seat activity peaked in the 1930s and line guide/tip-top

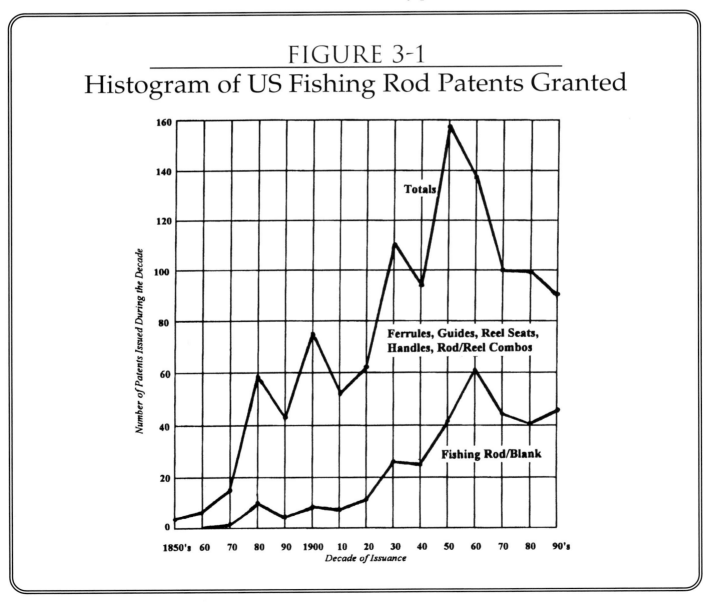

FIGURE 3-1
Histogram of US Fishing Rod Patents Granted

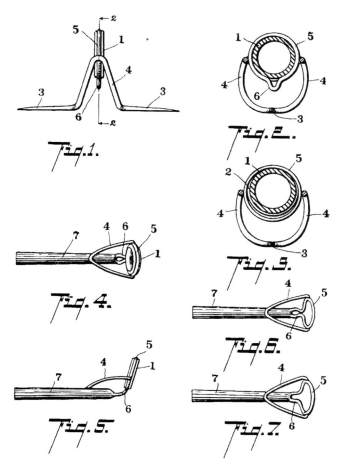

Shakespeare's Braced Guide Patent No. 958,775.

rod patents in the 1980s and 1990s being awarded to Japanese inventors and/or being assigned to Japanese companies (particularly Daiwa/Seiko, Shimano and Ryobi). This of course mirrors the situation throughout the United States in many other product areas. This should be a warning signal to any fly rod manufacturers who are not affiliated with an aggressive Japanese partner. In a more general sense, please note that fly rods are an internationally-marketed product. This study made no attempt to either tabulate or evaluate fishing rod

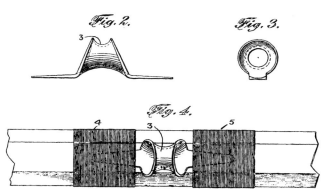

E.R. Davis' Bell Guide Patent No. 1,444,063.

patents in other countries because of the significant additional effort which that would require. I can't however leave this subject without suggesting that foreign patents by US rod companies should be an essential component of their international marketing strategy.

activity peaked significantly in the 1950s. There seems to be no unique reason for these peaks other than the fact that they were associated with the overall level of fishing rod patent activity.

The increased activity in ferrule patents in the 1880s and 1970s however is more readily explainable. In the 1880s there was significant development effort taking place at H.L. Leonard's shop and at his competitors' places of business. At that time, many new concepts were being studied to waterproof ferrules; i.e. to isolate the cane end from external moisture. Also, serrated, tapered and cushioned ferrules were being developed to soften the abrupt transition from cane to ferrule, to minimize stress concentrations. In the 1970s, graphite fly rod development was in its infancy, and all manufacturers were experimenting with ferrules made of this new, space-age material.

Another trend which I noticed while doing this patent study is the increasing number of US fishing

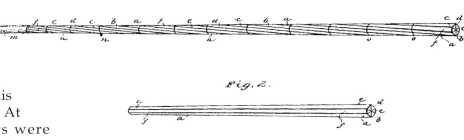

Fred Divine's Spiraling Strip Patent No. 476,370.

Trade Secrets

It must be emphasized that patents are just one way of protecting an inventor's or a manufacturer's technical concepts. A common alternative is to hold the concept as a trade secret and to maintain that secrecy for as long as possible or useful. The trade secret approach is quite practical when the invention cannot be deduced (reverse-engineered) from the final product and when the number and loyalty of employees justifies this strategy. And so, one shouldn't ever assess the technological strength of a company or an industry based upon only the size of its patent portfolio. In fact, perhaps the current level of fishing rod patent activity (nearly half of the 1950s time period) is being balanced by increasing attention toward trade secrets.

Conclusions

Finally, I must add another caution to anyone tempted to make snap judgments based on the statistical information presented in this chapter. The US patent system provides a reasonable degree of assurance that a concept embodied in a patent is novel and feasible.

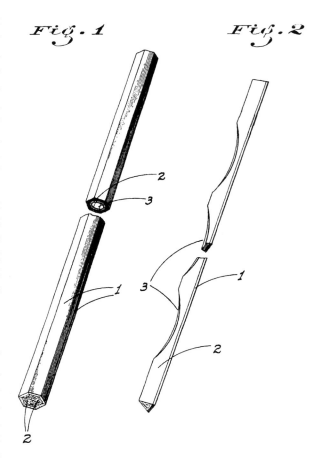

E.C. Powell's Hollow Cane Rod Patent No. 1,932,986.

There is however no such assurance that the concept is either practical or marketable. My past experience with patents and this recent study have taught me that the truly significant patents are highly outnumbered by patents which are impractical, trivial or prohibitively expensive (admittedly, both of my two US fly rod patents fall into the latter category). I'll even go out on a limb and guess that only 5 to 10 percent of all of the 1101 fishing rod patents identified in this study are truly significant when measured against the test of time. In the event that someone would like to carry this study further, and confirm or deny this assertion, I have enclosed Tables B-1 through B-6 in Appendix B, which list all of the patent numbers of these 1101 patents.

Dreiser's 1883 rod/reel combination. US Patent No. 283,084.

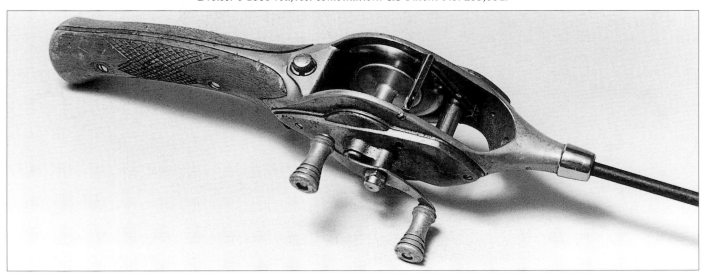

Chapter 4
FLY ROD MANUFACTURING PROCESSES

There are a broad range of manufacturing processes that have been used to fabricate fly rods. This chapter will generally describe those processes most used by industry, plus a few of the more popular variations thereof. Interspersed with the text are sketches and photos which should assist the reader in understanding the written descriptive material. I am indebted to the Orvis Company, for letting me photograph various sequences of their cane and graphite manufacturing lines.

Cane Fly Rods

Many man hours of labor go into the manufacture of a good cane (bamboo) fly rod. Although modern techniques have helped somewhat to lower cost and improve quality, the cane-rod making process has not materially changed in the past century. Since nature's materials are subject to more variation (both dimensions and physical properties) than materials that are man-made, labor skills have

Selecting the raw culms.

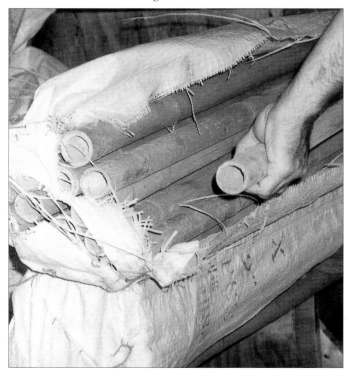

to be much more refined to produce a satisfactory product. A few too many strokes of the file or careless glue application can relegate the cane-in-process to the scrap heap.

The cane culms are first carefully selected from stock, with emphasis on straightness, lack of surface defects and general cosmetics. Strips of cane are then cut or split from the culm, grouping these strips together for further processing so that all strips are likely to have the same stiffness and strength characteristics. Some cane-rod makers

The split culms.

flame or bake the raw culm or groups of raw strips, to change their appearance and improve their physical properties. The strips are also positioned together so that the cane nodes are staggered when finally assembled as a rod blank. Then the strips are all cut to their final length, the outer enamel

---

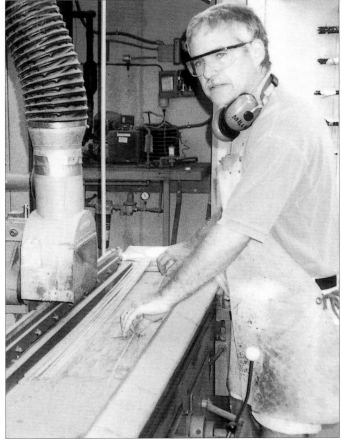

Milling the splines.

matched strips. Each of the strips is then machine-tapered, removing all of the useless interior pith and excess cross-section. Finally, the strips (now called splines) are precision-milled into their final triangular, tapered shape. Many individual rod makers skip the initial rough-machining stage, instead electing to shave each strip into its final, triangular and tapered shape with a hand plane and special fixtures. This is exceptionally painstaking work, since the final dimensions of the tip end of a spline may be as little as 1/32 of an inch on each of its three sides.

Final inspection.

surfaces are cleaned and the nodes are filed so that they are flush with the surface of the rest of the strip. At this stage the six-foot culm has been reduced to a group of three-foot to five-foot

Usually, each of the two blank sections (butt and tip) are assembled from six splines, though both four- and five-sided cane rods are still being made today in very limited quantities. Glue is applied to both mating surfaces of each spline and the six splines are tightly bound together with two opposing helical wrappings of a strong twine. The blank section is then rough-straightened by hand and maintained in a straight position while the adhesive sets. After the adhesive joints are fully set, the twine is unwound from the blank and the blank's surfaces are stripped to remove all excess adhesive and the natural enamel of the splines' outer surfaces. Then, the blanks' ferrule-ends are machined and the nickel-silver ferrule halves are glued in place. The final precision fit of the ferrules is achieved with a very fine file. This can be done either before or after the ferrules are glued in place. The fly rod blanks are then spined, matched

Binding the splines.

and subjected to a final hand-straightening after localized heating over an alcohol burner. At this stage, most manufacturers add several highly-thinned coats of varnish on the blank. Some also add a coat or two after the rod is fully assembled.

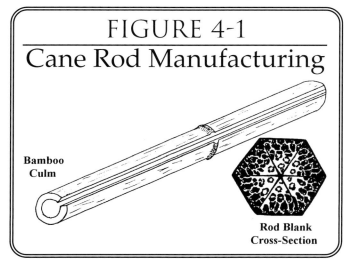

FIGURE 4-1
Cane Rod Manufacturing

Bamboo Culm

Rod Blank Cross-Section

In the final stages, cork rings are glued onto the butt, the grip is turned and sanded to its final dimensions, and the reel seat is fitted and glued in place. The line guides, tip-top and hook keeper are then wound in place using silk or nylon thread. The final step is to coat the thread wraps with a color preservative (optional) and one or more coats of a relatively viscous varnish or polymer coating. And thus, the modern cane rod has been converted from a raw culm of Tonkin cane to a precision fishing instrument, per Figure 4-1. In a typical production shop it will have gone through the hands of many skilled artisans, but in many shops all of these steps will be carried out by one person.

The microstructure of a finished cane rod is depicted in Figures 4-2A through 4-2D, at degrees of magnification ranging from 6x to 200x. Note that in the 100x and 200x microphotographs one can easily see that each individual cane fiber is hexagonal in shape. I suppose that this represents the ultimate justification of the six-strip cane fly rod, as compared to its four and five-strip competitors. At least that's what the late Tom Maxwell (co-founder of the Thomas & Thomas Rod Company) said when I showed him these photos nearly 30

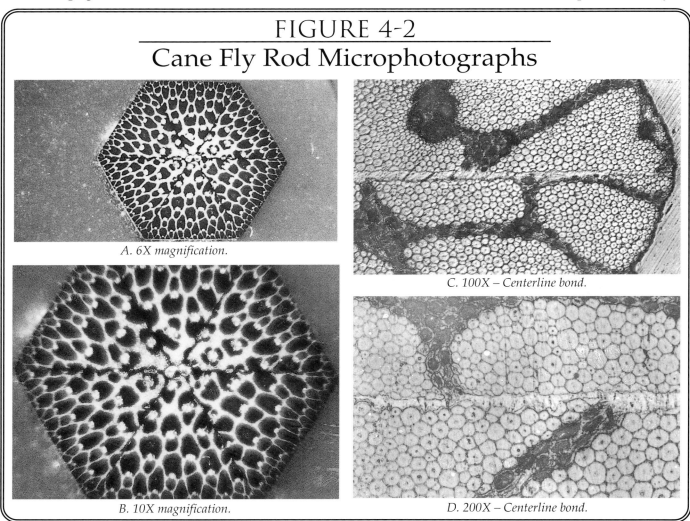

FIGURE 4-2
Cane Fly Rod Microphotographs

A. 6X magnification.

B. 10X magnification.

C. 100X – Centerline bond.

D. 200X – Centerline bond.

years ago. Actually, these photos illustrate a natural phenomenon which occurs when fibrous structures grow from adjacent nucleation sites. In the photos you can see the nucleation site of each fiber; a dark area at their center. Also, note that the smallest-diameter fibers are nearest the outer diameter of the culm, where the stiffest and strongest fibers reside. In metallurgy, a similar phenomenon occurs when some molten metals cool, forming an HCP (hexagonal close packed) crystalline structure.

Fiberglass Fly Rods

Fiberglass fly rods provided the first opportunity to mimic the natural power fibers of cane by using glass fibers produced by man. Glass fibers are produced by first heating raw glass blocks (silicon dioxide) until the glass is molten. A spinning wheel or drum is lowered into the molten glass, drawing fibers out of the melt so that they quickly cool and solidify. From this stage, the fibers are either gathered into yarn, collimated into a rope and/or woven into cloth. The fibers are usually coated with a sizing to ensure a good bond with the resin. Fiber groups are also often impregnated with resin during intermediate processing stages, to facilitate handling and to minimize the presence of voids or un-coated fiber surfaces in the end product.

Fiberglass fly rods have been manufactured by three distinctly different processes. Currently, nearly all fiberglass fly rods are made using one or more variations of the Conolon/Havens process, which uses a finely-tapered, removable steel mandrel as the foundation for a hollow rod blank. (See Figure 4-3). A polyester resin-impregnated fiberglass cloth is tightly wrapped around the steel mandrel and then over-wrapped with shrink tape. The cloth consists of mutually perpendicular glass fibers, with a very high percentage of these fibers oriented parallel to the mandrel centerline. The shape of the cloth pattern, which is basically a long right triangle with its sharpest point cut off, determines the final taper of the fly rod. Figure 4-4 shows some of the pattern shapes which are often used for fly rods. Note that all five of these cloth patterns are depicted with the same pattern width at both the tip end and the butt end. Even if each of these patterns were wrapped onto identical steel mandrels, their performance would be quite different from one another because of local differences in stiffness, weight and aerodynamic profile.

After the shrink tape is wrapped onto the green uncured blank, the blank and mandrel are hung vertically in an oven and cured at temperatures up to 250 or even 350 degrees F. During curing, the resin first becomes very liquid and the shrink tape

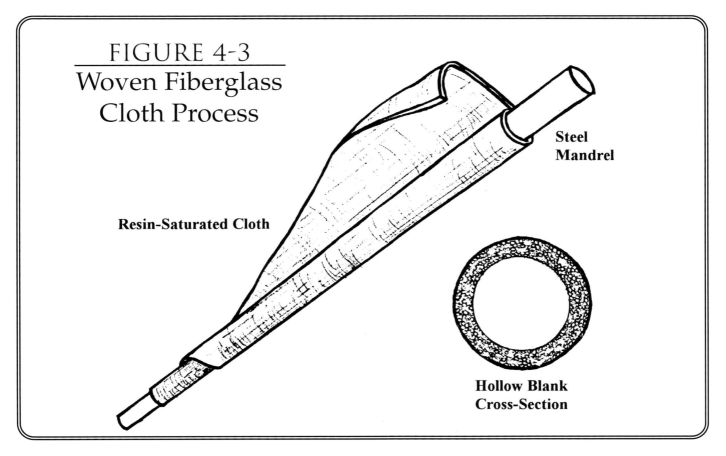

FIGURE 4-3
Woven Fiberglass Cloth Process

Steel Mandrel

Resin-Saturated Cloth

Hollow Blank Cross-Section

FIGURE 4-4
Typical Fiberglass Cloth Patterns

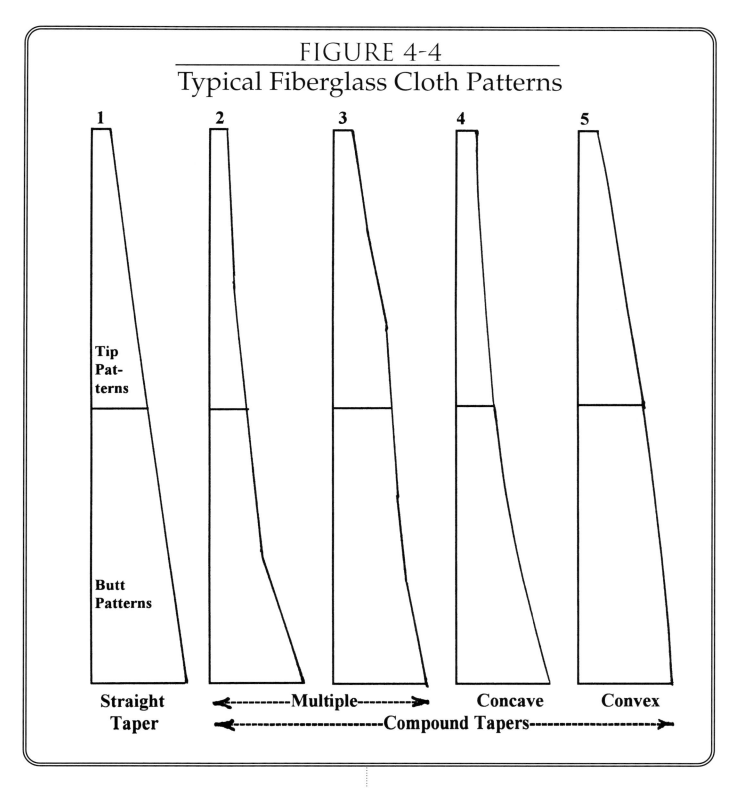

compresses the blank, squeezing out excess resin. During the final curing phases, the resin hardens, locking the fibers into a composite matrix having the final properties of a fly rod. After curing and cool-down the mandrel is removed, the shrink tape is removed and the blank is lightly sanded in a centerless grinder to remove the ridges left by the shrink tape. Ferrules are either integrally wrapped with the green blank or assembled after blank curing. With either approach, the mating ferrule surfaces are precision ground to form a tight-fitting joint with a very shallow taper. The blank's final color is achieved either by including the pigment in the resin system or by dip-coating.

The Shakespeare-Howald process is another technique used for manufacturing fishing rods. This is like the original Howald process except that the inclusion of a removable steel mandrel results in a hollow rod blank. Note the process sketch depicted in Figure 4-5. First, a unidirectional fiberglass rope impregnated with resin is helically wound around the mandrel, to provide the hoop strength necessary for all hollow structures subjected to bending loads. Then, resin-saturated, collimated fiberglass fibers are applied over the helical wraps. All of these collimated fibers are aligned with the mandrel axis, providing the requisite longitudinal resistance to bending stresses. During the process some of the fibers are cut and a variable-diameter die squeezes the blank down to its final tapered profile. Shrink tape is again used to confine the blank during curing. Although very well suited to high-volume

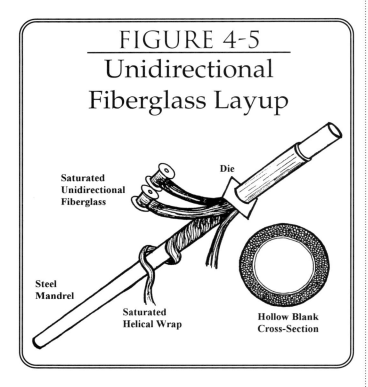

FIGURE 4-5
Unidirectional Fiberglass Layup

Saturated Unidirectional Fiberglass

Die

Steel Mandrel

Saturated Helical Wrap

Hollow Blank Cross-Section

production with its attendant low costs, this process is not very suitable for fishing rods requiring considerable tip flexibility. Accordingly, its application to fly rods is quite limited.

Another fiberglass fishing rod manufacturing process has found only limited application to fly rods, because of the relatively heavy weight of the final product. As shown in Figure 4-6, this pultrusion process is actually a continuous-casting process, resulting in a solid, constant-diameter fiberglass-resin rod whose length is limited only by the amount of resin-impregnated fiber that an be stored on the supply spools. The continuous rod

is directed through a curing oven, emerging fully hardened. The rod is then cut to the desired lengths, with each piece then individually shaped on a centerless grinder to its final tapered dimensions. Although relatively heavy compared to an equivalent hollow structure, these solid fishing rods are quite popular for some fishing applications because of their indestructible character.

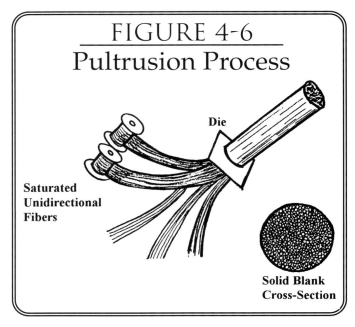

FIGURE 4-6
Pultrusion Process

Die

Saturated Unidirectional Fibers

Solid Blank Cross-Section

Boron Fly Rods

The raw material for boron fibers is the common commercial product Borax, a scouring powder. After being mined in the Death Valley California area, Borax is treated to form boron trichloride, an intermediate compound used to formulate a rocket propellant additive. Gaseous boron trichloride is also used in the production of boron fibers, in a reactor as shown in Figure 4-7. An electrically-heated fine tungsten wire is slowly drawn through the reactor, in an atmosphere of gaseous boron trichloride and hydrogen. Elemental boron is electro-deposited onto the tungsten wire, converting the wire into a tungsten boride core which is fully encased in layers of pure amorphous boron. Figure 4-8 is a microphoto of a typical boron fiber (0.0056 inches in diameter) clearly showing its characteristic corncob-like exterior. The principal reason why boron has not found wide application in sports equipment is the high capital costs of these reactors, the high cost of the raw materials and the relatively slow wire drawing speed.

For handling and processing convenience, the boron fibers are collimated on a paper tape, surrounded by a partially-cured epoxy resin and

FIGURE 4-7
Boron Fiber Reactor

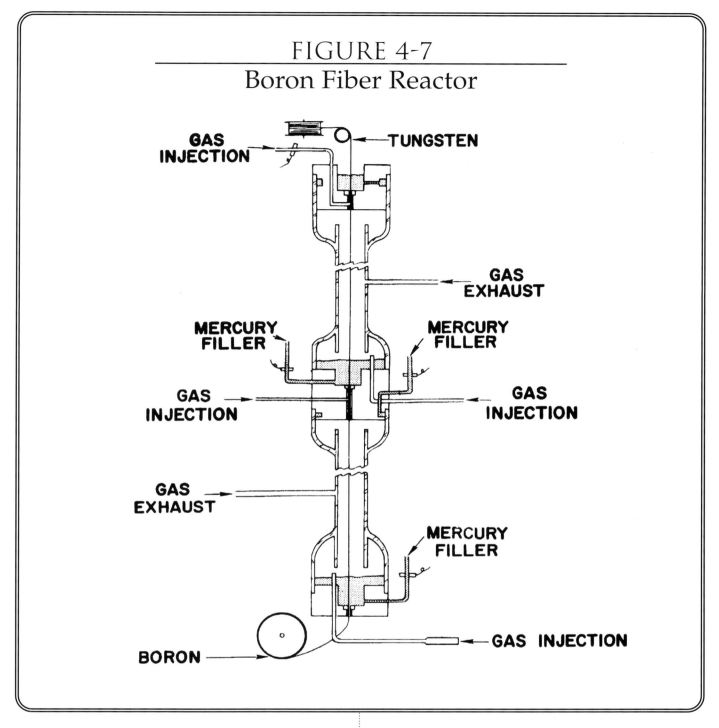

covered by a fine fiberglass scrim cloth. The tape is stored on rolls, with each inch of tape width containing 200 boron fibers running the full length of the tape. The tape is stored at 0 degrees F, to keep the tape's resin from drying out and losing its tackiness.

The first practical boron fly rods, manufactured by yours truly, copied the original work of Hewitt and Howald. A finely-tapered, circular balsa wood core served as a permanent lightweight mandrel. Narrow strips of boron-epoxy tape were laid up over the balsa wood and the green blank was over-wrapped with cellophane tape before curing. Although very lightweight, this configuration was very fragile. Figure 4-9 depicts the process eventually used to fabricate most of my boron fly rods. A group of five boron fibers served as a permanent mandrel. A boron/epoxy tape pattern was manually wrapped around this mandrel, which was weighted and hung vertically to provide a straight foundation for the green fly rod blank. After wrapping, all boron fibers remain exactly parallel to the

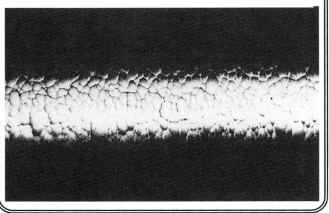

FIGURE 4-8
Boron Fiber Microphotograph (100x)

mandrel and fly rod axis. Some of my earlier rods also incorporated a single layer of graphite/epoxy tape, to improve surface cosmetics and to provide stress relief to the exterior boron fibers. Prior to oven-curing at 350 degrees F, the green blank was enclosed within nested sections of polyolefin shrink tubing. During curing, the resin saturates the boron fibers in the mandrel, forming a solid rod blank. After curing, the shrink tape was stripped off the blank, readying it for the usual finishing steps. These rod blanks have an interesting combination of fine-diameter tips for delicate

presentations and a structure which defies any attempt at lateral crushing.

Before permanently closing the doors of my rod shop in 1985, I experimented with another manufacturing approach which I think has potential merit for the future. Figure 4-10 shows this approach, which was first publicly disclosed in Reference 29, Table A-5. This concept consists of a conventional solid boron/epoxy tip, a new type of hollow butt, and a nickel-silver ferrule designed to provide an effective transition between these two sections. The hollow butt employs nested Teflon cylinders as the removable mandrel. The Teflon expands significantly during curing, providing a squeezing force which complements the shrink tubing in draining excess resin. This approach, which could use either boron/epoxy or graphite/epoxy tape, achieves higher fiber volume fractions and thus lighter weight for the same stiffness profile. Although I only made one of these rods, it remains my favorite for fly-fishing medium-sized trout streams.

During the 1970s, many of the larger rod manufacturers fabricated and sold fly rods composed of varying mixtures of boron, graphite or fiberglass fibers. To the best of my knowledge, all employed a hollow construction, using a removable steel mandrel. Figure 4-11 depicts the approach used by the Orvis Company, consisting of inner layers of boron/epoxy tape over-wrapped with layers of graphite/epoxy tape.

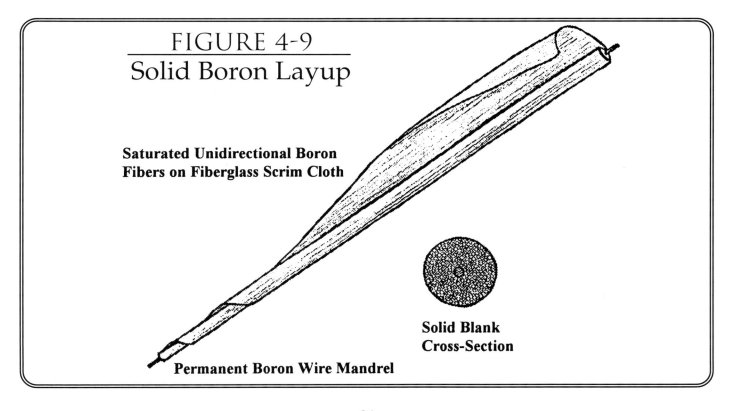

FIGURE 4-9
Solid Boron Layup

Saturated Unidirectional Boron Fibers on Fiberglass Scrim Cloth

Solid Blank Cross-Section

Permanent Boron Wire Mandrel

FIGURE 4-10
Another Approach

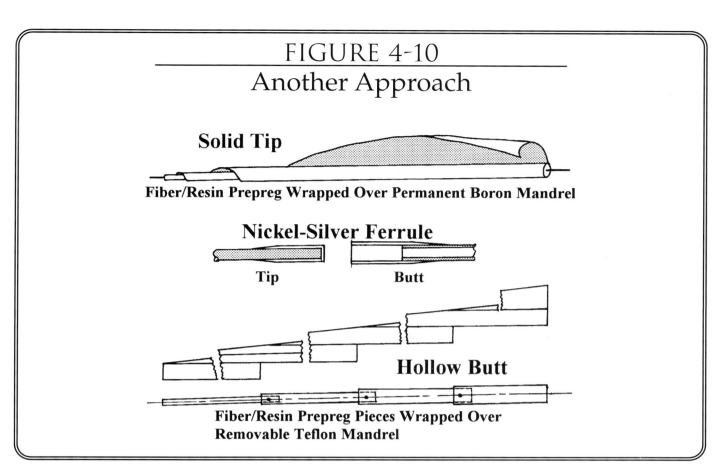

Solid Tip

Fiber/Resin Prepreg Wrapped Over Permanent Boron Mandrel

Nickel-Silver Ferrule

Tip　　　　　**Butt**

Hollow Butt

**Fiber/Resin Prepreg Pieces Wrapped Over
Removable Teflon Mandrel**

FIGURE 4-11
Boron/Graphite Layup

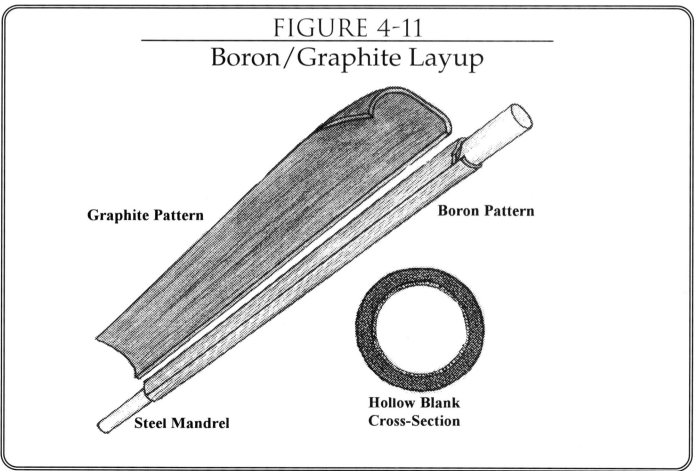

Graphite Pattern　　　　　**Boron Pattern**

Steel Mandrel

**Hollow Blank
Cross-Section**

Graphite Fly Rods

Today's modern graphite fly rod is fabricated using many of the technologies developed from the manufacture of fiberglass fly rods. Both fiberglass and graphite fly rods are most often made by wrapping a resin-impregnated fiber pattern over a tapered steel mandrel and curing the green rod in a high temperature oven. Figure 4-12 depicts a typical graphite fly rod manufacturing approach. We'll first review the ingredients of this process and then discuss some of the many variations used in the industry.

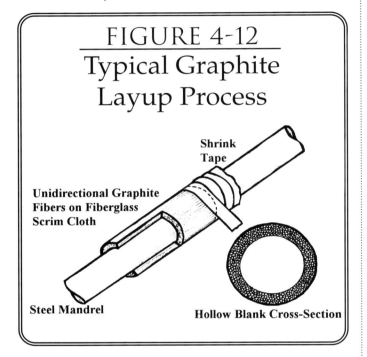

FIGURE 4-12
Typical Graphite
Layup Process

Shrink Tape

Unidirectional Graphite Fibers on Fiberglass Scrim Cloth

Steel Mandrel

Hollow Blank Cross-Section

Cutting the pattern.

Graphite fibers are produced by a heating and stretching a precursor at temperatures from 2000 to 3000 degrees C. Although rayon and pitch have been successfully used as precursors, superior strength and stiffness properties are achieved with polyacrylonitrile (PAN) fiber precursors. During the pyrolytic process all of the fiber material's constituents are driven off except for carbon, which is converted to its crystalline form, graphite, at temperatures in the range of 3000 degrees C. Graphite is highly anisotropic, that is its maximum physical properties are reflected in only one direction relative to its crystalline structure. Stretching at many times its original length aligns the graphite's microstructure to achieve these exceptional properties. Thousands of these pure graphite fibers, each less than a thousandth of an inch in diameter, are lightly coated with a resin sizing and then combined into a yarns or tapes, to facilitate handling and further processing.

A "few" mandrels.

Pattern/mandrel assembly.

Multiple strands of graphite fibers are impregnated with uncured epoxy resin, collimated onto a wide paper tape and backed with a fine dernier fiberglass cloth, or scrim. This graphite/epoxy tape is stored on rolls in a freezer to maintain tack and freshness. All of the graphite fibers are oriented toward the long direction of the tape, with the fiberglass scrim having enough lateral fibers to provide sufficient hoop strength in the hollow fly rod structure. Some manufacturers work with a tape having graphite fibers interwoven in the lateral direction. With sufficient numbers of these lateral graphite fibers, the fiberglass scrim is not needed.

The overall process for fabricating graphite fly rods is very similar to the earlier processes used to manufacture fiberglass fly rods. After the graphite/epoxy tape is removed from the freezer and allowed to come to room temperature, it is rolled out flat on a table where a predetermined pattern is cut. The uncut long edge of the pattern is then attached to the steel mandrel using a heating iron and the resin's natural tackiness. With the graphite/epoxy pattern attached to the steel mandrel, the assembly is placed on a specially-designed rolling table whose upper and lower surfaces move to squeeze the pattern and roll it on the mandrel. The tackiness of the resin keeps the

pattern tightly wrapped on the mandrel. The green blank is then tightly wrapped with a shrink tape, to provide further compaction during the curing process. After curing, the shrink tape is

Rolling the blank.

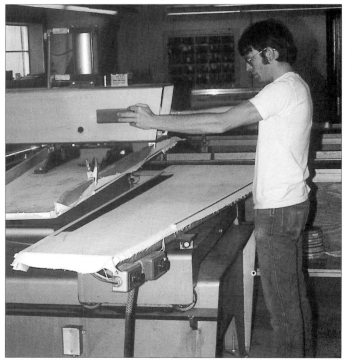

stripped off and the blank surface is carefully ground to remove the excess resin on the blank's surface. Currently, nearly all manufacturers follow these basic steps, or variations thereof.

Graphite, fiberglass or aramid (Kevlar™) fibers can also be wrapped helically, either directly on the steel mandrel before the pattern rolling or after the rolling operation and before the shrink tape wrapping. Again, these alternatives can be useful in providing fly rod hoop strength.

Removing the mandrel.

Dip-coating the blank.

Shrink-tape wrapping.

Chapter 5
FLY ROD DESIGN REQUIREMENTS

In Chapters 6 through 8, materials characteristics and design alternatives will be covered. Before getting into these technical topics however it's important that we first cover the foundation for all of these subjects; the design requirements for fly rods. These are the specifications that fly-fishers define, so that rod manufacturers can produce equipment that will sell in the marketplace. Just as important, these design requirements or specifications form the basis for purchasing decisions by fly rod buyers.

The purchase of a fly rod by a beginner is a most daunting experience. There are so many manufacturers, brand names, models, lengths, line weights, materials, actions, etc. that even an above-average intellect can be swamped by information overload and contradictory claims. Experienced fly-fishers also can be intimidated by this decision-making process, unless they thoroughly define beforehand *how the fly rod will be used.* And often, some design requirements can be in direct conflict with some others. For example, some fly-fishers might prefer a short fly rod for casting in tight quarters when fishing a brushy mountain stream. And yet, in that same environment they might at times also prefer a longer rod for better line mending or dapping. Thus, at the moment of a purchase decision, the best choice is nearly always a compromise amongst many alternatives. Another factor which significantly affects fly rod selection, perhaps more important than all other factors, is personal preference. A fly-fisher might for example *prefer* to use a six-weight outfit on a small spring creek, even though most would use a four- or even a three-weight fly rod.

Whenever a difficult decision or a complex analysis is involved, it's often useful to break the problem down into smaller pieces in order to better illuminate the key issues. Accordingly, the remainder of this chapter will be subdivided into six major fishing considerations; line weight, casting, line handling, setting the hook, landing the fish and general handling. Although I believe these to be the six principal areas appropriate for technical discussion, I would be remiss if I didn't acknowledge the existence of several other factors which will influence or even dominate the process of selecting a fly rod. These include price, appearance, warranty, service life, friends' recommendations and other factors which tend to defy objective analysis.

Line Weight

The design of a fly rod is affected by many variables, but the most important is the weight of the fly line to be used. When the fly rod and line are not properly matched, the angler is forced either to significantly adjust their casting stroke or to have more or less of the fly line extended beyond the rod tip, so as to properly flex the rod. The line-weight standards were derived more than three decades ago by the American Fishing Tackle Manufacturer's Association (AFTMA) to replace the confusing alphabet soup designations that were used in the preceding years. ATFMA decided to establish a series of numerical classes of line weights, based on the weight of the first 30 feet of fly line extended beyond the rod tip during casting. Originally, 12 classes of line weight were established (1 through 12), each usually expressed in grains (one ounce equals 437.5 grains). Allowances were also established to account for manufacturing variations, approximately +/- 10% for the Class 3 line and reducing to +/- 3 % for the Class 12 line. Figure 5-1 (following page) lists these line-weight classes, plus more current data now being debated for the 0, 13, 14 and 15 line-weight classes. Though somewhat arbitrary and far from perfect, these standards have served the fly-fishing community quite well over the past decades.

Generally, the size and/or pulling power of the fish will determine the line weight best suited for a fishing application. Figure 5-2 (page 43) shows the typical line weights most appropriate for the more common fly-fishing target species. When a species is identified with more than one line-weight grouping, this is usually due to significant species size variations, angler preference, fly size or other factors associated with the fishing location. It is

FIGURE 5-1
Fly Line Weight Standards

30-Foot Weight in Grains

Line Class #	Nominal Weight	Allowable Weight Range
*0	56	54-58
1	60	54-66
2	80	74-86
3	100	94-106
4	120	114-126
5	140	134-146
6	160	152-168
7	185	177-193
8	210	202-218
9	240	230-250
10	280	270-290
11	330	318-342
12	380	368-392
*13	450	435-465
*14	500	485-515
*15	550	535-565

* Not yet standardized

interesting that in most cases the rod is designed to fit the line weight which is best for the application, considering such important issues as presentation delicacy, casting distance, leader dimensions, fly size, etc. This generality though is definitely not applicable to the heavyweight rods used for tarpon, large tuna, sharks and billfish. These fly rods are designed primarily to turn and tire these large species of fish. The line weight is actually matched to the rod, to flex the rod sufficiently for comfortable casting.

Ted Leeson wrote a most interesting magazine article several years ago (Table A-5, No. 53), in which he described a study he undertook to compare line manufacturer's line weights. He took literally dozens of lines, cut them into 1-foot sections, weighed each section, and then determined how many feet of each fly line were required to fit it into the line-weight classes established by AFTMA. The objective was to illustrate that different weight lines could be used with the same rod, provided the weight of the line portion extended beyond the rod tip was within the class rating for that rod. He goes on to recognize that although these differing line lengths might not cast exactly the same, they were reasonably equivalent and well within the skill range of the average angler. I've certainly found that his claims are true for one or two greater or lesser line classes, and I know that many others have confirmed this through their own experimentation.

In Figure 5-3 (page 44), I have reconstructed a portion of Leeson's data, showing the line lengths for four manufacturer's lines in seven weight-forward classes. Note that there is a modest though not appreciably large variation from the 30-foot standard. As an example of how this data can have a practical use, consider the Scientific Angler WF6F line, which weighed out to the standard 160 grains for the first 30 feet of line. Using Leeson's charts, this same weight was measured with the first 45 feet of SA's WF4F line and with the first 23 feet of their WF8F line. If those variable lengths are within the skill capabilities of the angler, his fly rod can be effectively used for a much wider range of fishing applications.

Casting

The casting character of a fly rod is very dependent on the person who is doing the casting. One fly-fisher's perfect fly rod might be another's broomstick or buggy whip. One can appreciate this by examining the mechanics of casting. Chapter 9 covers this subject in considerable detail, but for the present purposes we can simply point out that the basic premise of a good cast is that the fly rod tip must travel more or less in a straight line during both forward and rearward casting strokes. This premise is fundamental because, until released by the angler, the line always follows the rod tip. If the tip wobbles, the line has waves in it. If the tip describes a semicircular path (with the high point directly overhead), the line will follow

FIGURE 5-2
Species/Line-Weight Chart

Line Weight / Fish Species	Ultra-Light - #0-#3	Light - #4-#5	Medium- #6-#8	Medium - Heavy #9-#11	Heavy Weight - #12-#15
Bluegills	X	X			
Trout, Grayling	X	X	X		
Bass, Carp, Pickerel, Walleyes		X	X		
Muskies, Pike, Salmon, Shad, Steelhead			X		
Ladyfish, Snapper, Sp.Mackerel, Pompano, Snapper Blues		X	X		
Albacore, Baby Tarpon, Black Drum, Bluefish,Bonito,Cobia, Bonefish, Cobia, Jacks, Snook, Redfish, Stripers			X	X	
Dolphin, King Mackerel, Permit, Trevally				X	
Billfish, Sharks, Tuna, Tarpon					X

FIGURE 5-3
Line Length Variations

Length in Feet For Weight To Equal Line Class Standard

Line Class	Std Wt. - Grains	Sci.Angler Ultra 3 WF_F	Cortland Lazer WF_F	Orvis Hy-Flote WF_F	Wulff Tri.Taper TT _/_
3	100	29	28	30	28
4	120	33	30	29	28
5	140	30	31	32	29
6	160	30	32	29	29
7	185	30	29	30	30
8	210	30	34	29	31
9	240	30	30	30	29

that path, ending up in a pile a few yards in front of the angler. The straight line motion of the rod tip, if in the right direction, pulls the line toward the target and minimizes distance- and accuracy-robbing wind-resistance losses.

So, what factors control the direction of motion of the rod tip? Figure 5-4 (page 44) contains many of the answers to this question. This stick figure is a kinematic sketch of an angler and fly rod at the midpoint of the forward casting stroke. The angler's objective is to move some or all of the links (body parts) so that the tip of the flexible rod moves approximately in a straight line. To do this one has lots of choices. Each of the links (lower leg, thigh, torso, upper arm, lower arm, hand and fingers) has the ability to be moved laterally and/or rotated. And let's not forget the joints that connect these links; the wrist, elbow, shoulder, hip, knee and ankle. Through a combination of experimentation, coaching and repetition the angler can develop an integrated movement of his casting linkages and joints so that the flexible rod tip

moves in a straight line. This is not an insignificant accomplishment, especially considering the fact that the flexural profile of any fly rod is continually changing during casting.

What happens though if the angler must use a fly rod which is either much stiffer or much more flexible? The casting stroke must be altered in order to obtain the same straight line tip travel. If the rod is either stiff like a broomstick or floppy like a strand of spaghetti, most anglers will not be able to move their body parts sufficiently to adapt to such extremes. All anglers are of course different in size and shape. Accordingly, their links or body parts are different with regard to length and strength and their ability to accommodate extremes of motion.

Angler size and shape are not the only personal attributes that affect the casting stroke. Some anglers prefer to use a rather slow and deliberate casting stroke while others work the rod and line back and forth at a rapid rate. The former tend to be more comfortable with longer and/or more flexible rods while the latter lean toward either shorter and/or stiffer rods. While I've noticed that taller anglers seem to fall into the former category, this is obviously not a hard and fast rule. In fact, the rate or frequency of rod oscillation is probably more dependent on the length of fly line extended beyond the rod tip during false casting.

Another factor related to the personal characteristics of anglers is their skill or athletic ability. Short fly rods require precise casting stroke timing in order to obtain the best in either fly delivery distance or accuracy. Long or short, relatively stiff fly rods require a similar precision in stroke timing. On the other hand, relatively long fly rods require a greater ability to guide the rod tip along a consistently accurate path for precision fly delivery. The longer rod amplifies any stroke errors made by the hand. Longer and more flexible rods also require a fairly subtle skill in stroke timing in order to produce tight casting loops, those trademarks of a controlled casting stroke with the potential for long casts. As shown in Figure 5-5 (opposite page), at position 2A, if the angler applies too much force too early in the casting stroke, the rod tip's inertia will cause it to dip downward and thus deviate from the desired straight line path.

The strength and stamina of anglers can also affect their ability to use certain fly rods. The use of a relatively short fly rod for repeated, long casts can be quite tiring because of the energy expended when rapidly moving the weight of the arms back and forth. The short rod requires the angler to

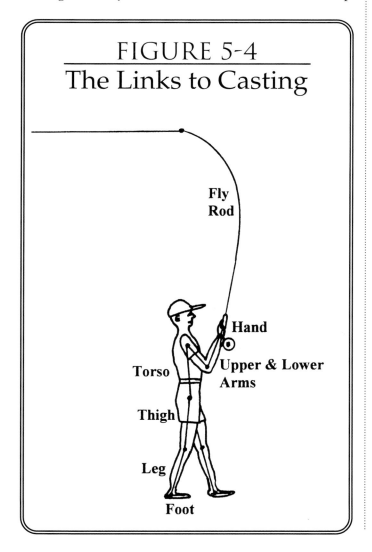

FIGURE 5-4
The Links to Casting

Fly Rod

Hand

Torso

Upper & Lower Arms

Thigh

Leg

Foot

move his arms either a greater distance or at a faster rate, in order to achieve line speeds equivalent to that obtainable with longer rods. Slow-action fly rods can also be less tiring than fast-action rods for repeated distance casting, for the same reasons. Long rods however can also be quite tiring, especially at higher line weights, because of the greater torque that has to be generated by the angler to accelerate the fly line to a given speed. Figure 5-6 shows that even greater torque is required with stiffer, fast-action rods, because of the longer *effective length* of the stiffer fly rod. Vince Marinaro noted this difference in effective rod length in Table A-3, No. 14, as did J.C. Mottram in Table A-3, No. 1. Another, more subtle characteristic of the stiffer rod may be its tendency to produce joint or tendon problems in the angler's casting arm because of the higher impact stresses. This phenomenon is quite similar to the "tennis elbow" problems experienced by tennis players who use relatively stiff or tightly-strung racquets. The above information clearly illustrates the importance of anglers' personal characteristics in matching a fly rod to their casting needs.

The types of casts that anglers must make will also determine the best fly rod for them. Distance casts of 80-100 feet will generally require a longer and stiffer fly rod designed for higher line weights. Highly skilled anglers can cast long distances with shorter, slower-action fly rods and lighter-weight lines but they are certainly the exception and not the rule. The equipment used by tournament distance fly-casters certainly gives valid testimony to this claim. When precision casting accuracy is required at short to medium distances, the shorter rod usually has the edge because, as mentioned earlier, the tip of the shorter rod has a lesser tendency to waver or drift outside of the angler's intended casting path. A somewhat stiffer rod also assists in casting accuracy, by permitting higher line speeds during cross-winds. Keep in mind however that shorter and stiffer is not appropriate when carried to extremes or under all circumstances. Casting a fly with a two-foot broomstick is certainly no way to achieve precision accuracy. And, if an angler is casting with only a few feet or yards of fly line extended beyond the rod tip, a fly rod is needed whose tip has enough flexibility to permit the achievement of straight-line rod tip motion without extraordinary casting stroke gyrations. Rod tip flexibility also assists in casting relatively wide casting loops, which are desirable to slow down terminal line speed for the most delicate of fly presentation.

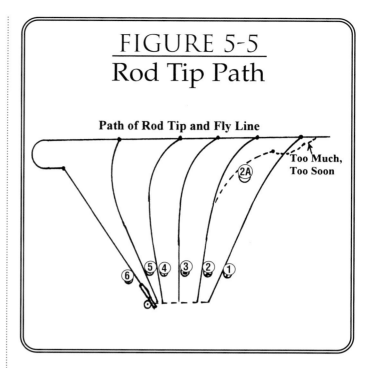

FIGURE 5-5
Rod Tip Path

Delicate presentations can indeed be made with a stiffer, fast-action rod, but it takes much more casting skill to achieve equivalent results.

The need for specialty casts can also favor certain fly rod characteristics. The reach, roll and Spey casts are much easier with longer fly rods because of the need to move the rod tip relatively long distances. A longer rod will also permit a higher back cast, when executing the steeple cast. Both single- and double-haul casts are facilitated with stiffer rods, because the rod tip won't deflect

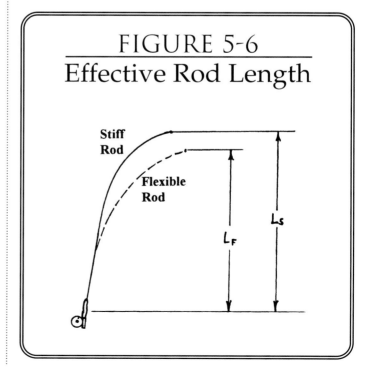

FIGURE 5-6
Effective Rod Length

too much when the haul is applied to increase fly line speed. The stiffer rod will also be helpful when executing the over-powered bounce cast, where the higher line speeds will create more bounce and therefore more slack line for control of fly drag. The short, flexible rod is quite helpful when the angler needs to use the bow-and-arrow cast in tight places.

The specific fly-fishing scenario can of course have a profound effect on the type of rod which best fits the circumstances. Short rods are preferred for mountain brooks where the foliage limits back casting opportunities. Longer rods are generally preferred when wading in deep water or while in a float tube, in order to keep the back cast from falling back onto the water, and are also helpful in clearing rearward obstructions during the back cast. Under windy conditions, a stiffer rod may be needed to develop sufficient line speed for either distance or accuracy.

The stiffer rod with its attendant higher line speed capability is often required in order to effectively cast wind-resistant flies. Poppers, muddlers, bass bugs and large saltwater flies certainly fall into this category. On the other hand, when casting heavily-weighted flies, a slower-action, more flexible rod is often the tool of choice to maintain an open casting loop for smooth fly delivery.

Line Control

Once the cast has been made and the fly has been delivered, the rod's next important function is that of line control. Frankly, I can't think of a single instance where the short rod is favored for this role. The longer rod facilitates line mending, fly relocation, roll pickups and any other manipulations required of either the line or the fly. Longer rods are capable of picking up more line from the water for recasting. The longer rod is especially useful when "high-stick" nymphing in trout streams. Here, the angler wades until he is reasonably close and cross-stream from a likely trout-holding lie. A very short cast is made diagonally upstream, so that the nymph will drift directly downstream into the target area. During the drift, the angler holds the rod very high (at arms length) at approximately 45 degrees, the rod tip generally following the drift while the line hand draws in slack line. This maneuver minimizes drag by keeping as much line out of the water as is practical. Also, with the line nearly vertical there is less opportunity for it to be in areas of differing stream velocity, a major cause for unwanted drag. High-stick nymphing is much less effective with a short

fly rod; it's impossible to place the rod tip almost directly over the trout's lie without getting so close as to betray your presence. The longer rod similarly facilitates reduction in fly drag when fishing a floating dry fly.

Setting the Hook

There is little doubt that the variables associated with casting usually dominate the decision-making process for rod purchases. Those variables associated with hooking and playing the fish however have got to rank a close second. Actually, I have misgivings about using the term "playing" because it might create visions of toying around with the fish until it is exhausted. I firmly believe that one should put as much stress on your tackle as is safely possible, in order to bring the fish in for release as soon as practical. You will note this predisposition throughout the remainder of this chapter.

There are many variables which affect the fly rod's ability to perform the hooking function, that is, the setting of the hook so that the fish can be brought to hand. The weight of the fish, the aggressiveness of his strike and the composition of his mouth parts are just those variables associated with the fish. Rod stiffness, especially tip and mid-section stiffness, is important whenever the leader tippet is fine enough to risk its breaking during the strike. A heavy fish will not be moved much by setting the hook, putting considerable stress on a fine tippet unless the rod is flexible enough to cushion the impact. A longer rod will also provide more cushioning during the strike, unless it is particularly stiff. Rod cushioning is similarly very important when the fish's strike is particularly aggressive.

This was made very apparent to me a few years ago while my son and I were float fishing the Clark Fork River downstream from Missoula, Montana. We kept two fly rods strung and ready while we floated downstream, taking turns with the rowing and fishing duties. One of the rods was a fairly flexible 9-footer for 4-weight and the other was a rather stiff 9-footer for 7-weight. The latter was often used when wind conditions required higher line speed to obtain a successful cast. If I was using the stiffer rod and we were moving downstream at a pretty good clip, a rainbow's strike in a backwater eddy would often break the fly off. I would set the hook fairly aggressively with the more flexible rod and then paid the price later when I forgot that I was using the stiffer rod. The same angler action with a heavier tippet, a lighter fish, or a situation where both angler and fish are not moving away from each other, might not have resulted in broken tippets. The subtle strikes of a nymphing brown trout or a sipping carp are also less apt to break tippets, even with a relatively stiff rod.

When retrieving a streamer or other baitfish imitation, the rod should generally be pointed directly at the fish and setting the hook normally consists of a strip strike with the line hand. This generally takes rod stiffness out of the hooking equation. For tarpon however and other fish with bony, hard mouth parts, the strip strike is usually followed by several rapid, lateral sweeps of the fly rod, to make sure that the hook point gets imbedded in a soft mouth area. For this situation, the rod should be as stiff as the leader tippet will permit, for optimum hook penetration. As in other circumstances, angler skill is an important consideration during hooking. If one can resist that natural instinct to rear back and yank the fish over one's shoulder, tippet breakage can be avoided by matching one's resistive pressure to the stiffness of the fly rod.

Landing the Fish

After the hook is firmly imbedded, the fly rod is next called upon to help the angler in bringing the fish in for release. For fish of any significant size and fine tippets, a rather flexible rod is preferred in order to put significant pressure on the fish and still have a cushion available when the fish makes sudden, darting motions. For extremely large or fast fish like tarpon, permit or bonefish, rod stiffness is irrelevant during the early stages of the struggle. The fish is going to run where he wants to until he tires and the angler's only options are to follow him and/or tire him via pressure from the reel drag or rim palming. Once the initial runs are over however, the more flexible rod again is preferred, to keep unrelenting pressure on the fish and still have a cushion to protect the leader tippet. The longer fly rod also assists in keeping constant pressure when the fish is darting back and forth in different directions.

When fishing for bass or snook where there are usually lily pads, mangrove roots or other cover, these obstacles can also give the fish an opportunity to break off by wrapping the leader around the obstacle. In this situation, the angler must exert whatever pressure is required to keep the fish away from such obstacles. He or she should prepare for such events by using leader tippets which are stout, and yet not so heavy as to impair fly presentation. Also, a rather stiff rod can be effective in turning the fish away from obstacles. When bone-fishing, the bonefish's path of flight will often take him past short mangrove shoots or coral heads which offer the potential for a break-off. In these circumstances, a longer rod can be most helpful in raising the line high enough to clear these obstructions. In general, however, it can be said that the shorter rod offers the opportunity to exert the maximum pressure or force, thus hastening the landing of the fish. This is why the stand-up tuna rods used in off-shore fishing are quite short. As has been pointed out by many fly-fishing authors, the reason for the ability to exert more force lies in the shorter effective length of the shorter rod. For example, if the angler is physically able to exert only a maximum of 20 foot-pounds of torque from his arm and wrist, a fly rod with an effective length of 8 feet can exert a line force of only 20/8 or 2.5 pounds. If the angler had a shorter rod with an effective length of 6 feet, his maximum applied line force will be 20/6 or 3.33 pounds. Clearly, the more flexible fly rod acts to shorten the effective rod length and thus increase available fish-fighting force.

The subject of maximizing line force is very important to our saltwater fly fishing down here in Southwest Florida, because of the size and stamina of some of our most sought-after game fish. Because of this, I conducted a simple experiment with the help of my wife and two friends. I set myself up with a fly rod in various fish-fighting positions, setting my camera on a tripod to record fly-rod position and shape while pulling on an imaginary fish anchored at ground level. The "fish" was located 10, 25 and 50 feet from my position, and the angle of the rod butt was varied at approximately 90, 40 and 20 degrees from the horizontal. An anchored spring scale was used to measure the line pulling force which I was exerting. For each combination of fish location and rod butt angle, two values of pulling force were recorded; one where there was just enough stress to put a small bend in the rod and another where I exerted as much force as I could sustain without either straining my wrist or risking rod breakage. Black-and-white photographs were taken of each test condition, and I later traced the principal features of these photos to obtain a series of sketches.

Figure 5-7 (following page) is a composite of three of these sketches, depicting the maximum rod stressing at a 50-foot distance, with the rod butt oriented at 90, 40 and 20 degrees from the horizontal. Note that the maximum sustainable pulling force increases from 1 to 3 pounds when

FIGURE 5-7
50-Foot Distance

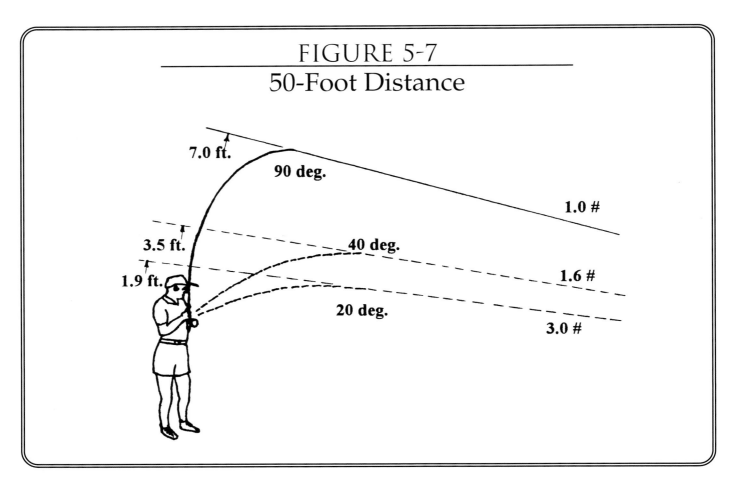

FIGURE 5-8
90-Degree Rod Angle

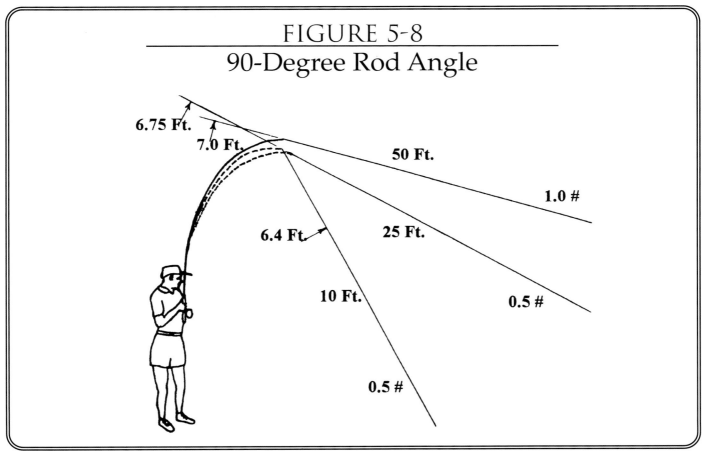

the rod butt angle is reduced from 90 to 20 degrees. This three-fold increase in fish-fighting pressure was achievable because the effective rod length was reduced by two-thirds. Please keep in mind that the effective rod length is not the distance between the angler's hand and the rod tip; it is the perpendicular distance between the hand and a line whose direction coincides with the line/leader pulling force. Thus, the torque on the angler's hand/wrist is the effective rod length times the line pulling force. The torque values calculated from the forces and lengths listed on Figure 5-7 are not the same because the angler's ability to exert torque varies at different hand positions. I found it much easier to exert 7 foot-pounds of torque with my wrist cocked upward in the abducted position, rather than exerting from 5.5 to 6.0 foot-pounds of torque with the wrist in the extended or adducted position. Nevertheless, the more uncomfortable, 20-degree rod butt orientation is much more effective in tiring a fish and bringing it to hand. Also, keep in mind that this shallow-angle rod orientation is just as effective when the rod is angled to either side as when it is angled slightly upward. In fact, when the side-angled pulling force is timed to change the fish's direction of travel, this multiplies the tiring effect on the fish.

Figure 5-8 (opposite page) is also a composite of three sketches, depicting rod-flex shape at the 90-degree butt angle for distances of 50, 25 and 10 feet. For the 10- and the 25-foot distances, the maximum line pulling forces were limited not by my wrist strength but by my concern for possibly breaking the rod tip. In these instances, the effective rod lengths are not very different from the effective length for the 50-foot condition. And yet the line pulling force is cut in half because of potential rod stress limits. Experienced anglers know that landing a still-active, large fish is one of the most dangerous scenarios with respect to fly-rod breakage. The problem is that the rod must be held more or less vertical so that the angler can bring the fish in close. And this occurs at a time when the fish sees the angler and the line pulling force has been drastically reduced. Certainly, an equation for impending rod stress!

Although all of this is useful information for anglers who hook and land large fish, what does this mean with regard to rod design and selection? Well, first of all this suggests that shorter rods are not only useful for exerting considerable pressure on large fish; they are also easier to manipulate without undue rod stress when landing the fish. A highly flexible long rod however can compensate to some degree for the problems intrinsic with long rods when fighting large fish. First, the effective rod length for a very flexible rod can be much shorter than for its stiffer counterpart. Therefore, more line pulling force can be exerted at the shorter length, even when holding the rod at the more comfortable upright position. Also, when bringing the fish in close, the more flexible rod will flex more deeply into the butt, moving the highest loads to where the rod is more capable of withstanding them.

General Handling and Use

The final topic which needs to be considered for fly-rod design requirements is that of general handling and use. As most fly-fishers are well aware, a high percentage of fly-rod breakage is due to handling accidents. Stepping on the rod, closing a door on it, stuffing the tip into the ground or into a ceiling fan or rapping it on a sharp rock are all common causes for the premature retirement of a functional fly rod. The ability of a fly rod to withstand the wear and tear of normal use is designed into the rod by the rod manufacturers. Unfortunately, the rod customer has no advance knowledge of the fragility or endurance life of the rod, except what he may learn from the experiences of his fellow anglers. Unlike aircraft parts, bridge structures and other hardware involving pubic safety, rod manufacturers don't work under a universal set of rules for design standards. They do however each have their own standards, and must pay close attention to this subject, especially because of the liberal warranties now prevalent in the industry. No manufacturer wants to take an extra quarter-ounce of weight out of a fly rod, to increase its marketability, only to have to replace most of these rods at no cost within the next few years.

The long rod is of course most susceptible to damage when being transported. Today's high-performance, multi-piece rods provide the angler with the ability to protect their investment by keeping them in cases until they are ready to be fished. Unfortunately, there will always be opportunities for breakage while walking in the corn field, through the woods or down the canyon path. You can't always have the rod case at your side.

Un-cased, the fly rod is vulnerable in four basic ways. First, it can be stubbed or otherwise bent beyond its breaking strength. This usually occurs in the tip area, where it's most vulnerable to over-flexing. Second, it can be stepped on, leaned against or in some other way crushed so that its circular cross-section can no longer sustain significant bending loads. Third, it can be struck with a hook point, sharp rock, etc. so that its outer fibers are fractured or cut. This constitutes a weak point and it can eventually culminate in a progressive crack and failure if this weak point is in an area subject to repeated high stressing. Fourth, it can simply be over-stressed during casting and fishing. Although this can result in an abrupt failure, it will often result in a future fatigue failure, where repeated stressing eventually weakens the rod so that it fractures at a stress level much lower than the original stress which precipitated the crack. To the best of my knowledge, rod manufacturers currently don't perform any kind of endurance testing to determine the fatigue strength characteristics of their designs. Perhaps that will change in the future, as competition nudges everybody toward increased technical prowess.

This chapter has attempted to identify all of the major requirements that are relevant to the design of a fly rod. As I indicated at the outset, many of these requirements are in conflict with each other. And some are not applicable for some anglers' uses. And so you can see the complexity of the overall specifications that need to be considered by the rod manufacturers. What inevitably occurs of course is that the manufacturers make the problem more tractable by designing fly rods for specific and narrow applications; for tarpon, for bonefish, for bass in lakes, for trout in spring creeks, for trout in brawling western rivers, etc. But there are still subsets of design requirements which are very imprecise if not downright contradictory, reflecting the *personal preferences* of individual anglers. Therein lies one of the most significant challenges to the fly-rod designer; to design a fly rod for a specific application that will perform to the delight and satisfaction of the greatest number of flyfishers who fish under those conditions.

Chapter 6
MATERIALS PROPERTIES

In May 1973, an article which I had written was published (Table A-5, No. 2) entitled "A New Era of Fibers for Fly Rods." To the best of my knowledge, it was the first public writing which introduced the fly-fishing community to the use of boron and graphite fibers for fly rods. The article's title was a natural lead-in to its content, since at that time fiberglass fly rods were near the height of their popularity and bamboo fly rods were (and still are) preferred by many fly-fishers. Bamboo fly rods get their stiffness and strength from the natural fibers of the cane, imbedded in a matrix of lignin. Earlier fly rods made from greenheart, hickory, etc also relied on their woody fibers for their performance. Thus, all good fly rods over the years have been constructed from fibrous composite materials. I don't consider the metal fly rods manufactured in the 1940s as "good" fly rods.

The Special Characteristics of Composites

This isn't just a coincidence. A fundamental attribute of ultra-small-diameter fibers is that they can be synthesized by man (or grown by Mother Nature) with a minimum of the microscopic defects which degrade their physical properties.

Figure 6-1 tabulates some of the more important physical properties of current high-performance fibers. We'll be getting into these properties in more detail later in this chapter, but for now I just want to make note of the fact that some of these fibers (steel, boron and graphite) have been synthesized in the experimental laboratory and tested to have ultimate tensile strengths exceeding one million psi. These accomplishments have been achieved with extraordinary process control and in relatively short lengths, making them currently too expensive for practical commercial applications.

Accordingly, if exceptional strength and stiffness is needed in a light material, composites incorporating very small-diameter fibers are likely to be the best approach. Bulk materials, whether cast, forged, extruded, drawn or machined, inevitably have microscopic defects which will lead to fracture or unacceptable distortion when highly stressed. And so, man has copied Mother Nature by "growing" very small-diameter fibers and placing them in a resin matrix where each fiber can carry its share of the load. The role of the surrounding resin becomes clear when one considers how a fly rod would behave if it consisted of just a bunch of loose longitudinal fibers. Each fiber

FIGURE 6-1
Fiber Tensile Properties

Fibers	Ultimate Strength - PSI	Elastic Modulus - PSI	Density - lbs./cu.in.
Fiberglass - E Glass	500,000	10.5 Million	0.092
- S Glass	650,000	12.6 Million	0.090
Graphite - Hi Strength	760,000	40.0 Million	0.063
- Hi Modulus	400,000	52.0 Million	0.067
Kevlar	400,000	19.0 Million	0.052
Boron	500,000	55.0 Million	0.090
Steel	300,000	30.0 Million	0.285

would be free to bend on its own, and without any lateral restraint the entire structure could be bent into a tight circle, offering little bending resistance. By comparison, when confined in a resin matrix the fibers on the inside of the bending arc don't buckle under the local compressive forces and the fibers on the outside of the bending arc cannot laterally drift toward the neutral centerline of the rod. If the resin maintains its tenacious grasp of all fibers, the composite will behave as an integral structure.

Whether the fly-rod structure is hollow, solid, circular or polygonal, the composite behaves just like a conventional material, although at some fraction of the fibers' physical properties. This fraction follows what the designers call the "rule of mixtures"; i.e. the composite material properties are equal to the fiber properties multiplied by the volume fraction of the fibers oriented in the "working" direction. Thus, if the fibers make up 50% of the volume fraction of the composite (the resin constituting the other 50%) and if all fibers are oriented in the direction of the rod centerline, the rod's theoretical flexural strength will be 50% of the fiber's flexural strength. Carrying this one step further, if all the fibers in the rod were twisted as a group so that each was oriented at an angle of 45 degrees to the rod centerline, the rod's theoretical flexural strength would be 25% of the fiber's flexural strength, since all fibers are only 50% effective in the working direction.

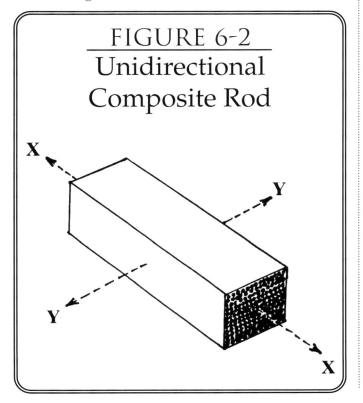

FIGURE 6-2
Unidirectional Composite Rod

Another unique property of fibrous composites is their ability to transfer loads between fibers by way of the bonding between the fibers and the resin. Consider the structure of Figure 6.2, a rod with a square cross-section, incorporating continuous, unidirectional graphite fibers (50% by volume fraction) in a resin matrix. If the graphite fiber's tensile strength is 500,000 psi, the rod's tensile strength would be approximately 250,000 psi. Now, suppose that each of the rod's thousands of graphite fibers were discontinuous, cut every inch or two along their length. If these discontinuities were completely random in location, so that only a few were effective in any given fracture plane, the rod would still retain much of its tensile strength and stiffness because adjacent intact fibers would take up the load of a broken fiber through shear forces transmitted through the resin. This phenomenon is the basis for an entire specialized field of composite materials—whisker composites. Perhaps some future fly rods will benefit from this technology.

The remainder of this chapter will cover the three materials properties which are the most important to the performance of the fly rod; stiffness, strength and density.

Stiffness

Stiffness is a material's ability to resist deformation when under stress. Its more technical term is modulus of elasticity, also sometimes called coefficient of elasticity or Young's modulus. A fiber's modulus of elasticity is measured in the laboratory by subjecting it to a tensile force, high enough to stretch the fiber but not so high as to fracture or permanently deform it. This stretching is thus within the material's *elastic* range; where the fiber returns to its original dimensions after the load is released. The standard formula for modulus of elasticity, E, is:

$$E = \frac{P/A}{e/L}$$

Where P = tensile load in pounds
A = fiber cross-sectional area in square inches
e = fiber elongation in inches
L = original fiber length in inches
E = modulus of elasticity in pounds/square inch(psi)

For a fiber, the *tensile* modulus of elasticity is usually the property of interest. A small-diameter fiber cannot be tested in *compression* because it will always buckle and render the test results useless. Also, determination of a fiber's lateral properties would be meaningless because of the impracticality of measurement and the fact that most of these fibers are anisotropic; they exhibit their exceptional properties only in the longitudinal direction. If you will recall from Chapter 4, the process for synthesizing graphite fibers involves considerable precursor stretching to adjust the carbon's molecular structure to align its strongest and stiffest orientation.

Thus, the orientation of the fibers in a composite structure is very important. Referring again to the square composite rod of Figure 6-2, note that all fibers are oriented in the X-X direction. If that rod were placed in a tensile testing machine and pulled in the X-X direction, the rod's tensile modulus of elasticity could be determined using the above formula. Let's assume that this composite rod is ten inches long, one-inch square in cross-section, and incorporates 50% unidirectional graphite fibers and 50% resin. Let's also assume that application of a 20,000-pound tensile load causes the rod to stretch 0.01 inches. The rod's tensile modulus of elasticity can be calculated as: $E = (20,000/1\times1)/(0.01/10) = 20,000/0.001 = 20$ million psi. That would suggest that the graphite fiber's tensile modulus of elasticity would be 40 million psi which is typical of the properties of some graphite fibers. One might logically ask why the modulus of elasticity of the resin isn't included in the above formula. The reason is that resin modulii are only a million psi or so and contribute hardly anything to the stiffness of a typical composite structure. For example, if the rod of Figure 6-2 were pulled in the Y-Y direction, the resulting deformation would reflect this very low modulus, since the graphite fibers would contribute nothing to its lateral stiffness. If however that shape rod were constructed per Figure 6-3, with alternate layers of graphite fibers oriented in both the X-X and Y-Y direction, the situation would be quite different. Here, the graphite fiber volume fraction could still be 50%, but 25% would be working in the X-X direction and 25% would be working in the Y-Y direction. In this instance, the rod material's tensile modulus of elasticity would be 10 million psi in *both* the X-X and Y-Y directions.

Unlike individual fibers, the rods pictured in Figures 6-2 and 6-3 have reasonable proportions of width to length. Accordingly, they have less of a tendency to buckle when subjected to compressive loads in the X-X direction. The compressive properties of most unidirectional fiber composites (per Figure 6-2) are however usually much less than their corresponding tensile properties. The reason for this is that even though each individual fiber is laterally supported by the surrounding resin, fiber

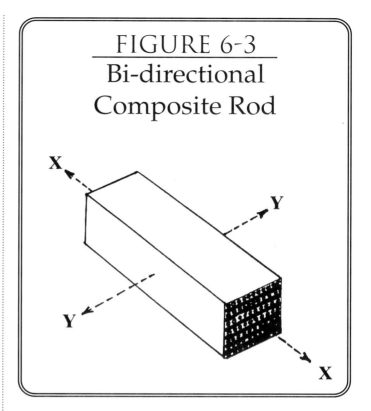

FIGURE 6-3
Bi-directional Composite Rod

microbuckling can still occur, destroying the fiber-resin bond and reducing both compressive modulus of elasticity and compressive strength. The compressive properties of bidirectional composites (per Figure 6-3) may still be somewhat less than their corresponding tensile properties, but the lateral fibers can assist the resin in restraining microbuckling in the longitudinal fibers.

Well, all of this talk about tensile and compressive properties is interesting, but how does this affect a fly rod which acts neither like a rope in tension nor a building column in compression? A fly rod is subjected to some rather complicated stress patterns, but the dominant source of fly-rod stress comes from bending. Figure 6-4 (following page) shows a simplified solid rod section being bent, and the forces acting on a typical cross-section. Note that under pure bending, the center of the cross-section acts like a fulcrum and is stress-free. The material toward the outer (convex) edge of the bending curve is subjected to tensile forces and the material toward the inner (concave) edge of the bending curve is under compression. Thus, during bending, both tensile and compressive forces are working, their magnitude being proportional to their distance from the rod centerline. The material's resistance to bending, its flexural modulus of elasticity, is the result of the combined tensile and compressive modulii of elasticity acting in their respective cross-sectional areas.

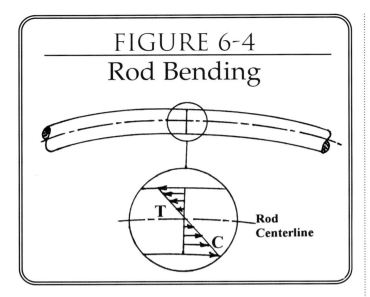

FIGURE 6-4
Rod Bending

Rod
Centerline

But a fly rod's ability to resist bending is not just a function of its material's flexural modulus of elasticity. Its cross-sectional geometry also plays an important role in determining the fly rod's stiffness. The fly rod's sectional stiffness is EI, the product of the material's flexural modulus of elasticity, E, and the rod's cross-sectional moment of inertia, I. A cross-section's moment of inertia is somewhat analogous to the wheelbase of a car. A car's lateral wheelbase helps to prevent the car from tipping over when turning a corner at high speed. Similarly, the "wheelbase" of the rod's cross-section helps to prevent excessive bending. The moment of inertia for a solid circular rod is determined by the formula:

$$I = \pi \ \frac{D^4}{64}$$

Where π = the constant 3.1416
D = the rod's outside diameter in inches
I = the rod's cross-sectional moment of inertia in inches[4]

EI is usually expressed in units of (pounds per square inch)x(inches[4]) which equals pound-inches[2]. Note that rod section stiffness is proportional to the rod's diameter to the fourth power. This means that relatively small increases in diameter will produce quite large increases in section stiffness. Another way to look at this is that the material in the center of the solid fly rod is really rather worthless as far as flexural stiffness is concerned. This is of course the reason why most modern fly rods are hollow; the elimination of a significant amount of internal weight is easily replaced by a small increase in outside diameter to obtain the same levels of rod section stiffness.

The moment of inertia of a hollow rod section is equal to the moment of inertia of a solid rod whose outside diameter is the same as the hollow rod's outside diameter, minus the moment of inertia of a solid rod whose outside diameter is the same as the inside diameter of the hollow rod. In equation form:

$$I_h = \pi \ \frac{(D_o - D_i)^4}{64}$$

Where: D_o = rod outside diameter in inches
D_i = rod inside diameter in inches

Over the years many different rod cross-sections have been successfully used, so let's wrap up this discussion of moment of inertia by identifying the equations for I for these other shapes. First, there is the square cross-section, whose I_s = $a^4/12$, where a = the width of each of the square's sides. And let's certainly not forget the hexagonal cross-section, the trademark of most cane rods. I_h = $0.5413a^4$, where again a = the width of each of the rods six sides. Also, a = D/2 for a hexagon, where D = the largest outside diameter of the cross-section (across the corners). The general equation which applies to all regular polygonal cross-sections (equal sides) is

$$I_p = \frac{A(6R^2 - a^2)}{24}$$

Where D_o = rod outside diameter
Where: A = the cross-sectional area of the polygon in square inches
R = the maximum radius (to the corners) of the polygon in inches
a = the width of each of the polygon's sides in inches

It should be remembered that the above equation applies whether the rod has 3, 4, 5, 6, 7, or even 99 sides and is independent of the orientation of the polygon (more on this subject in Chapter 7).

Let's not lose sight of the fact that a fly rod doesn't have just a single value of section stiffness but rather an infinite number of section stiffness levels, all different and significantly increasing from tip to butt. I like to call this rod characteristic its stiffness profile, the variation of EI along its length. Figure 6-5 depicts the stiffness profile of the first 80 inches of a 7 1/2-foot for 6-weight cane rod which I tested in 1972. Actually, I tested dozens and dozens of rods in this manner over the years and Figure 6-5 is quite typical of good 7 1/2-foot 6-weight rods of the 1970s. Note that the section stiffness varies between 20 and nearly 1800 pound-inches squared over the 80-inch distance. This dramatically illustrates the effect of diameter on fly-rod stiffness.

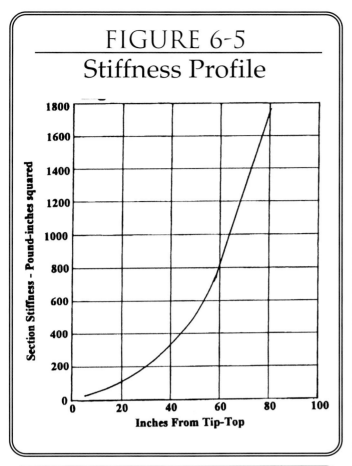

FIGURE 6-5
Stiffness Profile

Section Stiffness - Pound-inches squared vs. *Inches From Tip-Top*

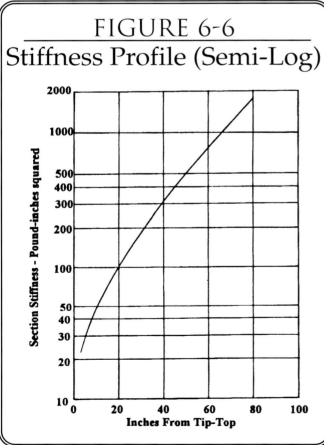

FIGURE 6-6
Stiffness Profile (Semi-Log)

Section Stiffness - Pound-inches squared vs. *Inches From Tip-Top*

For those readers who might want to get into stiffness profiling in more depth, note that Figure 6-5 is somewhat difficult to accurately read in the area of the tip, where the most accuracy is needed. For this reason, I've always used semi-log plotting paper (per Figure 6-6) to help in the plotting and analysis. Finally, for those who may be mathematically inclined, I've noticed that the stiffness profiles for better fly rods seem to generally follow the cubic equation:

$$EI = ax^3 + bx^2 + cx + d,$$

where x = the distance in inches from the rod tip and

a, b, c, and d are constants which are unique for any specific stiffness profile.

Before getting to the next section on material strength, it is important to emphasize a few points about rod stiffness. First, whenever I use (or have used) the term "rod stiffness," I am referring to the stiffness profile characteristics of the fly rod. It is a characteristic which is difficult to describe to the layman, but nevertheless is the only quantitative way to describe how a rod will bend during various casting and fish-fighting maneuvers. Knowledgeable anglers are forever talking about soft tips, stiff butts, etc. but these vague terms don't really mean much unless one can present this information in numerical terms. If a fellow fly-fisher tells me that his fly rod tip tapers down to a stiffness level of 20 pound-inches squared, that tells me very precisely how soft or how stiff it is. I strongly believe that there is a need for more quantitative standards in fly-rod specifications, so that the buyer can better understand what he is purchasing.

Another important issue to be recognized is that a rod's stiffness profile can be measured quite readily, without lots of expensive capital equipment. I will be saying more about this in Chapter 10. On the other hand, the variable which is quite difficult to directly determine is the material's flexural modulus of elasticity. The simultaneous influence of tensile and compressive modulii is most difficult to reconcile. And then add to that the additional effects of fiber volume fraction and fiber orientation and you have a very complex analytical problem. It is especially difficult when one considers that all of these variables can be changing throughout the length of the rod. In spite of this difficulty, the flexural modulus of elasticity can be determined after-the-fact, by determining the rod's stiffness profile through testing, by measuring the external and internal rod diameters, and then calculating the flexural modulus from the general formula: $E_f = EI/I$. Accordingly, rod manufacturers could gradually develop a data base which will eventually permit them to predict flexural modulus of elasticity based upon various combinations of fiber orientation and volume fraction.

Strength

In general terms, strength can be defined as a material's ability to withstand stress. When a material is stressed, a load in pounds (or tons, kilograms, etc) acts over an area of material, usually expressed in square inches. Thus, strength is usually specified in pounds per square inch. One of the designer's basic jobs is to make sure that enough material is present (enough square inches) to keep the stresses well below the strength limits of the material. When specified quantitatively, strength must be further defined as to the particular stress mechanism being resisted. Accordingly, the word "strength" is usually preceded by a more descriptive term such as tensile, compressive, flexural, torsional or shear. Also, further descriptors are needed to clarify whether the material's yield or rupture strength is being referenced. These terms will become clearer as we continue the discussion in this chapter.

Strength is analogous to engine horsepower in an automobile. You won't really know if your car has enough horsepower until you try to pass another car on a hill. Similarly, you won't know if your fly rod is strong enough until you try to turn a heavy fish during a run or attempt to obtain that extra ten feet with your double-haul. And I'm sure that your local tackle shop wouldn't appreciate it if you attempt to test the strength limits of one of their demonstrator rods. Accordingly, you have to rely on the fly-rod manufacturers to do their homework and not deliver rods until they have been adequately tested.

Earlier in this chapter we defined fiber stiffness (modulus of elasticity) and explained that this property is determined by subjecting the fiber to tensile testing. Let's take a closer look at this test by examining the load-elongation curve of Figure 6-7. This curve shows that as a fiber (or other material) is loaded, it at first stretches or elongates in proportion to the applied load. If however the fiber is loaded beyond its "proportional limit," it begins to elongate at a faster rate. Before reaching the "yield point," removal of the load would result in the fiber returning to its original length, without undergoing any permanent deformation. If the fiber is loaded beyond its yield point, it will undergo some permanent deformation and it will not return to its original length after removal of the load, instead following the dotted line path of Figure 6-7. Continuing to increase the load will eventually result in fiber fracture or failure, the point where the fiber's ultimate tensile strength has been exceeded.

Very high performance materials like graphite and boron are relatively brittle; that is, the slope of the initial load-elongation curve is relatively steep and it is often difficult if not impossible to differentiate between the proportional limit, the yield point and the fracture point, because they are all quite close together on the elongation curve. Graphite or boron fly rods seldom take a set or permanent deformation in service, but when they do the cause is invariably the fracture of some fibers or failure of the bond between some fibers and the resin matrix. Early fiberglass fly rods had a significant problem in this regard, because moisture gradually destroyed the fiber-resin bond over a period of time. Moisture and, to a lesser extent over-stressing, also causes sets in cane rods. Fortunately, the natural resins in cane can often be heated to correct the set and restore the integrity of the fiber-resin bond.

The most important strength characteristic of a fly rod is its flexural strength. Like its counterpart, flexural modulus, flexural strength is actually a composite of the material's tensile and compressive strengths, acting in concert across a common stress

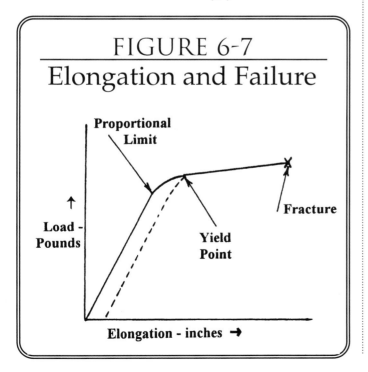

FIGURE 6-7
Elongation and Failure

plane. Figure 6-4 depicted the tensile-compressive stress relationship for a rod subjected to pure bending. Unfortunately, pure bending can be produced in laboratory test machines but it is seldom present in any real-life structures. Figure 6-8 shows all of the external loads imposed on a typical fly rod while stationary. This scenario simulates the circumstances of fighting a fish, though it also applies to hook setting and the early stages of line pickup. Here, the only loads imposed on the fly rod are the restraining force and moment (torque) applied by the angler's hand and the forces imposed on each of the guides by the fly line. Many writers describe this scenario as if the line were pulling on the tip. This would be the case only if the line were physically tied to the tip-top and thus prevented from sliding freely in the guides.

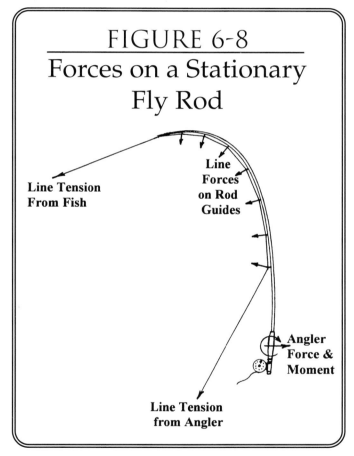

FIGURE 6-8
Forces on a Stationary Fly Rod

Line Tension From Fish

Line Forces on Rod Guides

Angler Force & Moment

Line Tension from Angler

The forces shown on Figure 6-8 impose a relatively complex stressing of the stationary fly rod. The most dominant stresses are due to bending, but there are many other stress modes that are operative. For example, note the line guide forces shown in Figure 6-9. The direction of the guide forces are always in a direction which bisects the angle of the line on both sides of the guide. Wherever the rod is bent, this means that the forces

of two adjacent guides are convergent; i.e. if extended, they would eventually intersect at a common point. This results in components of these forces which produce compressive stress in the rod section between the two guides. This compressive stress acts to relieve the tensile stresses on the convex side of the rod and to add to the compressive stresses on the concave side of the rod.

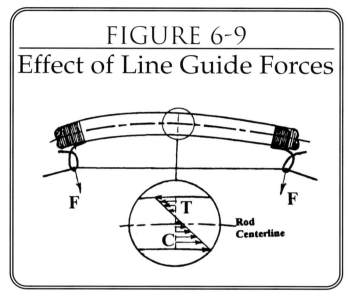

FIGURE 6-9
Effect of Line Guide Forces

F

T

C

F

Rod Centerline

Figure 6-9 shows how this compressive stress due to line guide forces changes the stress pattern in the cross-section, actually moving the neutral stress axis away from the geometric center of the rod. Since the compressive strength of many composites is already relatively low compared to their tensile strength, this could be an important factor to consider when predicting anticipated material strength limits for new rod designs. Figure 6-10 (following page) shows the external appearance of typical compressive stress failures that can occur when a fly rod is overloaded in bending. In the left-hand sketch, this is the likely failure mode for a composite composed of unidirectional fibers, with a helical under-wrap to provide its primary hoop strength. In the right-hand sketch, the rod is constructed from a cloth weave, containing integral helical fibers necessary for hoop strength. Although this type of composite might broom outward (as in the left-hand sketch), it will more often collapse inwards, this usually being the path of least resistance.

Thus far, we have examined the loads on a fly rod when it is relatively stationary. When the fly rod is used as a casting instrument it is moved or oscillated back and forth, sometimes at a rather rapid rate. Figure 6-11 (following page) depicts the loads on a fly rod as it accelerates through the

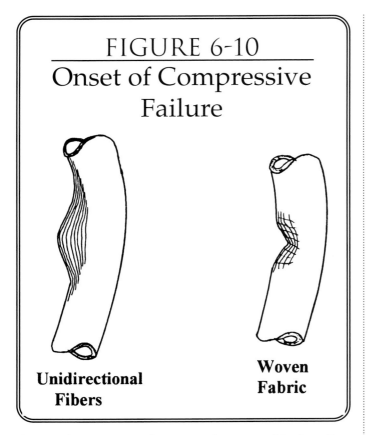

FIGURE 6-10
Onset of Compressive Failure

Unidirectional Fibers

Woven Fabric

forward cast, just a fraction of a second before line velocity and rod flexure are at their maximum. The angler is still exerting a force and a torque through the rod grip and a line pull from his line hand. The line tension he is exerting is however now matched by an equal and opposite force representing the

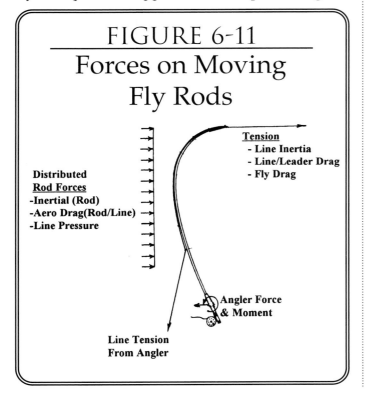

FIGURE 6-11
Forces on Moving Fly Rods

Tension
- Line Inertia
- Line/Leader Drag
- Fly Drag

Distributed
Rod Forces
-Inertial (Rod)
-Aero Drag(Rod/Line)
-Line Pressure

Angler Force & Moment

Line Tension From Angler

inertial forces of the line as it is being accelerated, plus the aerodynamic drag forces of the line, leader and fly.

The basic laws of physics tell us that any object at rest (the line is nearly at rest when it is fully extended on the back cast) exerts a restraining force when accelerated. This force continues during acceleration, but as soon as the line velocity stops increasing this force ceases to exist, even if line velocity is still quite high. And, of course, this inertial force begins again in the reverse direction once line velocity begins to decelerate. During line deceleration, however, this reversed inertial force often doesn't affect the rod since the line has decoupled itself from the rod during line shoot. At the instant shown on Figure 6-11, the line's inertial force plus the drag forces are imposed on the fly rod in a distributed fashion, since the line literally hugs the leading edge during the forward cast, when snake guides are used. Note that these distributed forces exist until the line angles up to enter the butt stripping guide. At that point, a portion of the load is transmitted to the stripping guide, just as in Figure 6-8. If ring-type guides are used and the rings are sufficiently raised, all line inertial forces are transmitted to the fly rod by way of the line guides. Again, let me remind the reader that the line's inertial and drag forces do not pull on the rod tip; they only pull against line/guide friction and the restraining force in the angler's line hand.

There are two other forces which are imposed on the fly rod during casting. The rod also has rod inertial forces acting on it, distributed throughout its length. Again, these forces exist only when the particular rod section is accelerating or decelerating, not when it is motionless or moving at a constant velocity. The direction of the force depends on whether acceleration or deceleration is involved. If you're standing on a bus, you will surely have a feeling for this direction when the bus lurches forward from a dead stop or screeches to a halt from normal running speed.

Another distributed force on the fly rod during casting are the aerodynamic or wind resistance forces which occur when the rod (especially the tip) cuts through the atmosphere. These forces are surprisingly large and are just as important as the rod's inertial forces. This will be discussed in further detail in Chapter 9. Contrary to the inertial forces, aerodynamic drag is directly proportional to rod velocity squared, whether or not acceleration or deceleration is involved.

All of the rod loads discussed thus far affect

the flexural stresses exerted throughout the length of the rod and hence also affects its flex profile. Many of these loads also involve shear stresses, which can be important in fly rod design. Shear stresses can be best explained by referring to Figure 6-12. Shown is a cantilever beam jutting out from a stationary wall. If a load P1 is applied at the tip of the beam, the maximum stress will occur at the base of the beam adjacent to the wall, since it will be subjected both to flexural stresses from bending and shear stresses from the load P1. If the only beam load was P2 (neglecting beam weight), the bending moment would be zero and the only beam stresses would be a shear stress caused by the load P2. If this load were to be progressively increased until beam failure, the beam would shear off flush to the wall, just as if someone had cut through it with a hand saw. The beam has now failed in shear and its vertical shear strength (in pounds per square inch or psi) is calculated as the load in pounds at failure, divided by the beam's cross-sectional area in square inches.

Vertical shear is generally not an issue in fly-rod design, because these forces are perpendicular to the orientation of most of the fibers and need to be very high before they can damage the rod's structural integrity. A notable exception to this statement occurs when a concentrated load is imposed at a particular point in a rod and if this load is large enough to overcome the hoop strength in the structure. Horizontal shear is however most important because the fibers are much more prone to separation from the resin matrix. Horizontal shear is often called interlaminar shear, especially when it results in fiber-resin separations caused by stress differentials in adjacent fiber layers. Horizontal shear under ferrules was a common problem in early cane rods, when moisture penetrated the cane structure to weaken the cane-nickel silver glue joint. This was particularly prevalent when the cane diameter was reduced somewhat to accept the cylindrical ferrule, reducing its section stiffness significantly below the section stiffness of the ferrule.

Torsional strength is most important in golf clubs, because of the substantial torque imparted to the club shaft during impact with the ball. In fact, golf club shafts are rated according to their behavior under torsion. Such is not the case with fly rods; the only conditions which impose torsion on the rod shaft are when the line guides are not in-line with the casting or fish-fighting plane. Fly-rod torsional strength is generally not a problem, unless the angler twists the rod to extremes while fighting

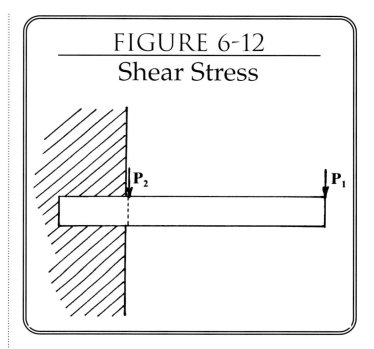

FIGURE 6-12
Shear Stress

very heavy or strong fish. However, since fly rods are not designed with much torsional stiffness, rod twisting during casting can introduce some serious lateral tip motion which will hurt both casting distance and accuracy. Rod twisting can be caused by an angler's errant casting stroke or by rod spine (more about spine in the next chapter).

Hoop strength is usually not defined in quantitative terms; nonetheless it is most important to fly-rod design. Hoop strength is achieved by having enough fibers oriented helically around the fly rod cross-section to prevent the tubular structure from collapsing in response to bending or lateral loading. As mentioned in the preceding paragraph, one such source of lateral loading occurs when you inadvertently step on a fly rod, crushing it if you're heavy enough or if the point of contact is highly concentrated. Hoop strength also comes into play when a fly-rod section is highly stressed in bending. The fibers on the outer, convex side of the bend are under considerable tension, exerting a lateral force on inner layers of fibers and tending to change the circular cross-section to an oval shape whose narrowest width is in the bending plane. This effectively reduces the cross-sectional moment of inertia, further increasing the bending and causing ultimate failure. With sufficient hoop strength, achieved by supporting or interlocking the longitudinal fibers with helical fibers, significant ovalization is prevented.

This discussion would not be complete without some brief comments on fatigue strength. Most fractures occur when the material's ultimate tensile, compressive, shear or flexural strength have been exceeded. When failure occurs after dozens or even thousands of loadings, all well under the material's ultimate strength limits, a fatigue failure is said to have occurred. Theoretically, fatigue failures won't occur because low-level stresses won't fracture the fibers, the resin nor the fiber-resin bonds. Nevertheless, in the real world, material defects do occur. These could be voids in the resin, unbonded fiber-resin areas, post-cure residual fiber stresses, etc. Whatever the cause, such defects can be the source of microcracks if they are in areas of significant stress. Microcracks can also be created by subjecting a defect-free fly rod to excessive stress in a localized area. The microcracks can gradually spread with repeated loading, and eventually grow large enough to cause a rod failure. The techology exists to conduct fatigue testing, to diagnose the causes of fatigue failures and to differentiate them from other types of failures, but to date the rod manufacturers have elected to not invest in this effort. This could change in the future, especially in view of the liberal warranties now being offered by the industry.

Density

Density is defined as the weight of a unit volume of material and is usually expressed in pounds per cubic foot, pounds per cubic inch, grams per cubic centimeter, etc. Density is of dominant importance when selecting the basic materials systems to be used in fly rods, because weight (inertia) has such a critical effect on casting performance. Fly rods are relatively long tools whose tips move at high, reversing velocities. Reversing directions creates very high inertial forces, which requires considerable angler skill when casting. Reductions in weight reduce inertial loads, improving casting performance. The graphite fly rod weight reductions accomplished over the past two decades is the principal reason why longer rods, longer casts and multi-line weight capability in individual rods are now available to the average fly-fisher.

With the lighter rods (and lighter reels) of today, even a nine- or ten-foot fly rod is comfortable for the average fly-fisher to handle. Even in those few instances where the rod may feel a little top-heavy in the hand, there are no good reasons to add compensating weight to the reel end of the rod. During the 1940s and 1950s, the metal fly rods were so top-heavy that anglers sometimes did add material to the reel to achieve a better static balance. While this may indeed have resulted in more comfort when simply holding the fly rod in horizontal position, it had to be detrimental to casting

performance because of the additional inertia imposed on the caster. Figure 6-13 illustrates this point. When fly-casting, the angler torques the rod-reel assembly in reversing cycles and the inertia of all rod and reel parts adds to his energy requirements for repetitive casting. Addition of more weight, anywhere, does nothing but make his job harder. I've heard that some anglers prefer this additional weight to help keep the rod stroke in-plane, for accuracy purposes. Although this does suggest some merit, I'd personally prefer the reduced energy requirements of the lighter assembly. Today's fiber and resin densities are improved over the past, but there may still be room for improvement in the future.

Other Material Properties

The hardness of the fly-rod material is another property which can affect its ability to perform to the satisfaction of the angler. Boron is very hard, graphite is very soft and fiberglass and cane fall in between. Hardness is primarily an issue when the rod is struck with something which is harder than the rod material. In the extreme, those critical outer layer fibers can be cut or fractured. Graphite's softness has thus far not inhibited its popularity, so this aspect may be of only academic significance. Other material properties like electrical conductivity, thermal expansion, thermal conductivity, etc. are similarly interesting but of no significant importance to the average fly-fisher.

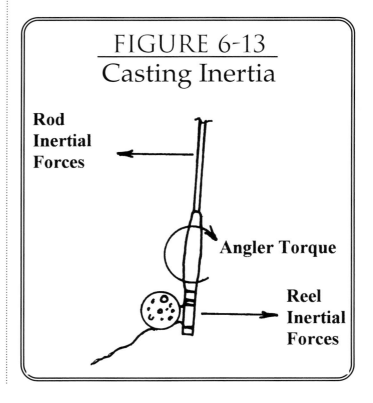

FIGURE 6-13
Casting Inertia

Rod Inertial Forces

Angler Torque

Reel Inertial Forces

Chapter 7
TAPER AND CROSS-SECTIONAL GEOMETRY

Whenever seasoned rod makers talk about one of their fly rods which has received customer accolades, they often explain their success is due to its special taper. If pressed for more detail, they will often change the subject or offer some foggy generalities certain to confuse the questioner. This tendency toward secrecy is logical, since any good businessman tries to protect an advantage he may have relative to his competition.

The earliest rod makers probably found it difficult to keep such secrets, since their tapers were readily measurable. And it was probably difficult if not impossible to hide the type of wood or cane used. However, rod makers who experimented with different internal reinforcements were surely able to literally bury their innovations. As experience grew with Calcutta and Tonkin cane, rod makers learned that the outside physical dimensions didn't tell the whole story. Careful culm selection, heat treatment, surface protection and node treatment all provide their unique signature on the final performance of a cane rod. Leonard, Payne, Orvis and all the early rod makers each devoted thousands of hours of experimentation to develop unique dimensional tapers and accompanying process variables that made their fly rods special to their clientele.

And so, the fly rod's outside dimensions often only partially define its fishing performance. When hollow fiberglass fly rods were introduced in the 1940s, a major hidden dimension was the outer diameter profile of the removable steel mandrel. Although these diameters could be determined simply by cutting up a fly rod and measuring its internal diameters, this takes time and effort. Similarly, every detail of a modern fiberglass or graphite fly rod can be measured by cutting it up into short sections and subjecting it to careful analysis. Fiber material, fiber volume fraction, fiber orientation, resin material, void content, etc. are all determinable, given the time and willingness to expend the effort.

Rod Taper

The rod maker's "taper" is thus the entire spectrum of process variables which contribute to fly rod performance. That certainly doesn't mean that such detail should be available or even of interest to the average fly-fisher or fly-rod customer. In fact, it's not even necessary to get down to that level of detail to fully understand a fly rod's benefits or how it compares to other fly rods. In its broadest sense, fly-rod taper can be defined as the shape and distribution of materials to produce a design which will efficiently cast the fly line and bring a fish to hand. This broad non-dimensional term can however be replaced by five fly-rod characteristics, each of which can be defined in quantitative terms; length, line weight, stiffness profile, diameter profile and inertial profile.

Of course, length and nominal line weight are standard descriptors for fly rods, but these two terms tell nothing about the rod's flexibility or casting performance. Stiffness profile may be a new term to some readers, but it is an objective way of quantitatively defining a structure's bending characteristics without attributing it to any one arbitrary loading condition. Because stiffness profile includes the effect of the rod material's modulus of elasticity, it takes into account such variables as fiber modulus of elasticity, fiber orientation, fiber volume fraction, resin material, and void content. Since stiffness profile includes the effect of cross-section moment of inertia, it also takes into account rod section external and internal diameter profiles. Accordingly, stiffness profile describes everything about a fly rod that affects its flexural characteristics under static (motionless) conditions.

Fly rods are however often in motion and such motion also affects the rod's curvature or flexural shape. The rod's external diameter profile defines the width of the path which the rod cuts through the air and thus the amount of aerodynamic resistance or drag force imposed on the rod during casting. In practice, the main area of aerodynamic interest is in the rod's tip section. The butt section is subjected to very low velocities and therefore its drag forces are quite low, in spite of the larger diameters. Their effect is also of lesser importance because they won't affect butt bending nor have a measurable impact on required angler casting torque.

Inertial profile is the other characteristic which affects the fly rod's dynamic performance. Inertial profile is simply the weight distribution of the rod along its length and again the weight or mass of the rod tip plays the dominant role in affecting rod curvature and angler torque requirements. The butt section's distributed weight affects angler torque requirements to a small extent, but the effect on rod curvature is negligible. Inertial profile or distributed weight is difficult and impractical to measure, but there are measurements which are good approximations of this variable. One is simply the weight of the tip section (of a 2-piece rod). The weight of the entire rod is not very useful in this context because butt section weight, including grip and reel seat, completely overshadow the weight of the tip section. Another useful measurement is the balance point of the assembled rod, while being loaded by a standard, simulated reel weight. The distance of the balance point from the rod grip is a good measure of how "top-heavy" the rod is and is quite similar to the standard measurement of swing-weight in golf clubs.

Cross-Sectional Geometry

Although the rod's "taper" is a multi-faceted characteristic whose constituents may be of little interest to the average fly-fisher, there is no question that the taper is the heart of the fly rod. It is *the* reason why fly-fishers fawn in reverence over a rod's ability to meet their every demand for casting performance. It is also often the reason for frustration and anger when its character is inconsistent with an angler's particular casting style. Rod makers achieve their unique tapers by varying the fly rod's cross-sectional geometry and the material structure within that geometry. As emphasized before, this is not a simple task, because of the huge number of variables that need to be considered and evaluated.

To demonstrate the effect of just a few of these variables, I've put together a little experiment. The stiffness level at the mid-point of an 8-foot/6-weight fly rod is usually around 500 pound-inches squared (whether the rod is made from cane, graphite, fiberglass or boron). Based on typical design assumptions, I determined the cross-sectional geometry for sixteen different cases, each case meeting the same requirement for a section stiffness of 500 pound-inches squared. The results are depicted in Figure 7-1. The most important design assumptions are listed below:

- All-longitudinal fibers with a 40% fiber volume fraction for the solid composites of boron, fiberglass and graphite

- Thin-wall hollow structures with a wall thickness of 0.050 inches
- Thick-wall hollow structures with a wall thickness of 0.100 inches
- All hollow structures (except for fiberglass-thin wall) using longitudinal fibers, with either scrim or a small amount of helical fibers for hoop strength
- Thin-wall fiberglass structure using woven cloth with an effective fiber volume fraction of 25%
- Other thin-wall structures with a fiber volume fraction of 40%
- Thick-wall structures with a fiber volume fraction of 45%
- An average cane modulus of elasticity of 6.23 million psi

The average cane modulus of elasticity of 6.23 million psi was based on testing which I performed in the 1970s. Although the modulus of the cane's outer fibers are much higher, I haven't seen any published data which would provide the basis for an estimate. Accordingly, there are no configurations shown for hollow cane structures, even though such rods have been available for many years.

Referring to Figure 7-1 (following page), note the significant differences in the sixteen configurations. Most important however is how these different configurations will affect the aerodynamic drag and the inertial forces on the fly rod. For each configuration, the numbers in the upper left-hand (clear) box represent the relative aerodynamic drag. Similarly, the numbers in the upper right-hand (shaded) box represent the relative inertial loading. Rather than include actual diametral and weight data (which wouldn't mean much to most readers), I have normalized each configuration relative to the lowest calculated value. Accordingly, the lowest inertial force with a 1.0 would be the high-modulus, thin-walled graphite structure and the highest inertial force with a 4.3 would be the cane structure. Similarly, the lowest aerodynamic drag with a 1.0 would be with the solid boron structure and the highest aerodynamic drag with a 1.75 would be the thin-wall E-glass structure.

If we were to directly compare the thin-walled structures of high-modulus graphite and S-glass, it can be seen that the inertial forces for the S-glass structure would be 23% higher. Also, the aerodynamic forces for the S-glass structure would be (1.66-1.08)/1.08 or 54% higher. This means that the S-glass rod would flex more than the high-modulus graphite equivalent during

FIGURE 7-1
Section Geometry Variations (500 lb-in^2)

(1/4 Inch = |←   →|)

Material \ Cross-Section Shape	Solid		Hollow Thick-Wall		Hollow Thin-Wall	
Cane (Hexagonal)	1.50	4.30	N/A		N/A	
Fiberglass - E-Glass	1.50	4.54	1.52	3.15	1.75	1.32
Fiberglass - S-Glass	1.44	4.04	1.45	2.90	1.66	1.23
Boron	1.00	1.83	1.03	1.80	1.07	1.33
Graphite - Hi-Modulus	1.02	1.48	1.03	1.34	1.08	1.00
Graphite - Hi-Strength	1.06	1.59	1.09	1.32	1.18	1.04

Air Drag Factor ☐   **Inertial Load Factor** ▨

casting, because of the considerably higher inertial and aerodynamic forces exerted on the tip section, in spite of its equal section stiffness. If we were to similarly compare the cane equivalent to the thin-wall, high-modulus graphite, the cane's inertial and aerodynamic forces are, respectively, 4.3 times and 39% greater. The purpose of this data is primarily to demonstrate that configuration choices can have a profound effect on casting behavior and thus must be considered at the outset, to ensure the design of a fly rod with good dynamic performance.

Polygons and Circles

Aficionados of cane fly rods have debated the pros and cons of the circular, square, hexagonal and pentagonal cross-sections for fly rods over a century. In the absence of today's knowledge of mathematics and engineering, most of the early debates were punctuated by baseless claims and incorrect assumptions. Much of this dialogue hinged on the stiffness and stability properties of the corners and flats on the cane. In Table A-3, No. 10, McClane reported that in the early twentieth century, rod-builder Robert Crompton became so embroiled in these arguments that he hired a mathematician to sort out fact from fiction. The mathematician proved that any regular polygon (equal-width sides) will exhibit the same moment of inertia in all planes of orientation, no matter where the corners and flats are located.

Many years ago, I asked my good friend and mathematician, Dr. Walt Arnoldi, if he would verify or disprove this theory. After only about an hour or two of effort, he showed me the mathematical proof that this claim was indeed correct. Figure 7-2 provides further, though qualitative, support. The solid line hexagon depicts a typical cane fly rod cross-section, where the line guides would be located on either the upper or lower flats and the X-X axis would be the neutral axis of bending. This rod's resistance to bending, its sectional stiffness, is as described earlier; the product of the material's modulus of elasticity and the cross-section's moment of inertia (E times I). Since the moment of inertia of a hexagon equals 0.5413 a^4, where a equals the width of one of the sides, it should be independent of how the hexagon is oriented relative to the axis of bending.

Now, note the dotted hexagon on Figure 7-2, which depicts how the cross-section would appear if the rod were rotated thirty degrees. Now there are two corners on the top and the bottom, which might lead some to believe that the moment of inertia has increased because these corners (A and B) extend beyond the flats, at a larger diameter. Although this does create an incremental increase of moment of inertia or wheelbase, this increase is offset by the incremental decreases in moment of inertia at G, H, J and K. It can thus be seen from Figure 7-2 that the increases in moment of inertia, due to the shaded triangles at A, B, C, D, E and F are exactly balanced by the losses in moment of inertia due to the triangles at G, H, J, K and at the axis of bending. Although each of these twelve triangles are equal in area, their differences in distance from the neutral axis of bending requires a mathematical exercise in plane geometry to verify equivalence in moment of inertia. This was the contribution provided by Crompton's mathematician and by Dr. Arnoldi. This analysis should also apply to hollow cane rods, provided both their exterior and interior surfaces are symmetrical regular polygons.

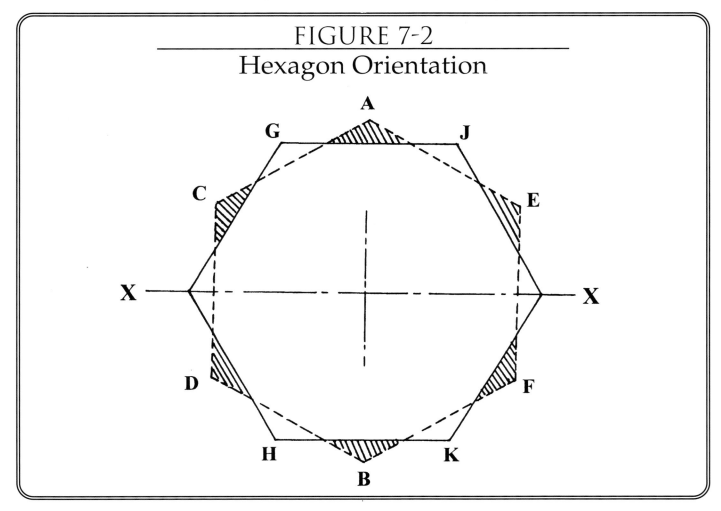

FIGURE 7-2
Hexagon Orientation

Of course, all of this is true only if the cane rod cross-section is fully symmetrical, with respect to both their dimensions and their physical properties. Variations in glue-line thickness might be sufficient to affect symmetry. Certainly, variations in the stiffness properties of any of the six splines would affect symmetry. Since the outer, smallest diameter fibers of the natural cane culm are much stiffer than those fibers located well below the culm's outer surface, this inherent stiffness gradient could produce non-symmetry if the splines were selected from different culms. The node locations in cane rods will also cause varying degrees of non-symmetry, no matter how carefully their dimensions are controlled. Although it's important to understand the basics of mathematical theory, it's essential to have an appreciation for how the real world can mitigate the usefulness of such theories.

Another debate which has continued over a century within the cane fly-rod community is the optimum number of sides on a cane rod. Obviously the acceptance of the six-sided configuration over the years has at least partially answered this question. However, I'd like to revisit this arena briefly, to make a few points. First, it would seem that the technically-optimum configuration would be one that provides the most stiffness, with the least weight and aerodynamic profile, and with satisfactory structural integrity. If we again assume a nominal section stiffness of 500 lb-inches squared and an average cane modulus of elasticity of 6.23 million psi, the required cross-sectional moment of inertia, I, can be calculated as 80.3×10^{-6} inches^4. Using this as a baseline, the outer and inner diameters and cross-sectional areas can be calculated for several cane rod configurations. And, assuming a typical average cane density of 0.043 lbs/cubic inch, the weight per inch of length can be calculated for each configuration. Figure 7-3 shows the results of these calculations for 4-, 5-, 6-, 7-, 8-, and 12-sided polygons and for the polygon with an infinite number of sides, the circle. Like Figure 7-2, Figure 7-3 lists the normalized values of all configurations in comparison to the most efficient. Also shown is a sketch of each configuration, with the line guides assumed to be located on the bottom (at 180 degrees), in the plane of bending.

FIGURE 7-3
Polygon Comparison
(I = 80.3 x 10^{-6} inches^4)

Shape Data	Square	Pentagon	Hexagon	Heptagon	Octagon	Dodecagon	Circle
Sketch	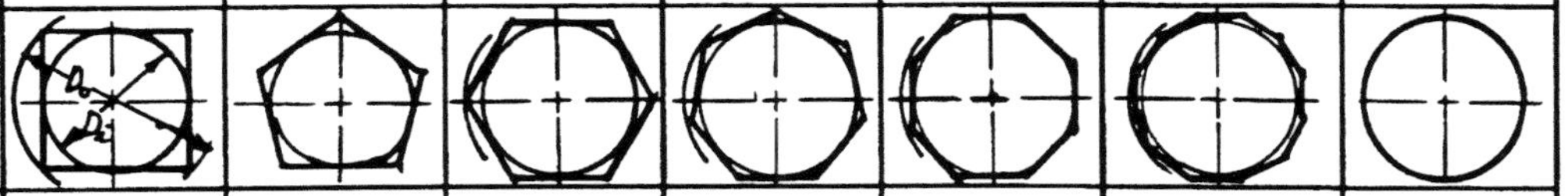						
No. Sides	4	5	6	7	8	12	∞
Side Width- in.	0.176	0.135	0.110	0.093	0.081	0.053	N/A
Outside Dia.- in.	0.250	0.230	0.220	0.216	0.212	0.206	0.200
Inside Dia. - in.	0.176	0.186	0.191	0.194	0.196	0.199	N/A
Normalized Weight - lbs	1.00	1.00	1.03	1.03	1.03	1.03	1.03
Normalized Profile - in.	1.00	1.31	1.26	1.19	1.11	1.13	1.14
Normalized Stress - psi	1.00	1.31	1.09	1.22	1.11	1.13	1.14

Referring to Figure 7-3, the most surprising information is the relatively insignificant differences in weight per inch for each of the seven configurations. This demonstrates how closely moment of inertia and cross-sectional area relate to each other for symmetrical planar shapes.

Comparison of the normalized data for aerodynamic profile shows that aerodynamic drag varies all over the place. The reason for this is that there are actually four different factors reflecting their impact. First, the overall diameter decreases slightly as the number of sides increase. Second, the square, octagon and dodecagon have flats at the sides (90 and 270 degrees) and therefore their aerodynamic widths are simply their inner diameters. Third, the hexagon has corners at 90 and 270 degrees and its aerodynamic width is therefore its outer diameter. Fourth, the pentagon and heptagon are not symmetrical at the 90- and 270-degree positions and their aerodynamic widths are therefore less than their outer diameters and yet greater than their inner diameters. It should be emphasized that although these data on aerodynamic width or profile suggest a proportional relationship to aerodynamic drag, this has not yet been proven by test to the best of this author's knowledge. In rod tip sections, where drag is most pronounced and important, the rod's aerodynamic behavior is governed by turbulent flow conditions, and differing cross-sectional shapes may not precisely follow geometric logic.

Another comparison shown on Figure 7-3 is the relative stress levels inherent in each of the seven configurations during bending. In Chapter 6, it was pointed out that the stress in a rod undergoing bending is zero at the neutral axis (90 and 270 degrees) and a maximum at 0 and 180 degrees. The equation for bending stress is:

$$S = Mc/I$$

where S = Bending stress in psi,
M = Bending moment in inch-pounds
c = Distance from the neutral axis in inches and
I = Cross-section moment of inertia in inches[4]

In our premise for Figure 7-3, we assumed a constant moment of inertia of 500 lb-inches squared. If we further assume the same moment (inch-pounds) exerted on each of the seven rod configurations, then the bending stress level is directly proportional to the distance, c, from the neutral axis. Or, stated another way, the maximum stress due to bending is always located at that point in the cross-section furthest from the neutral axis of bending. For the seven configurations considered in Figure 7-3, this highest-stress location is always at either 0 or at 180 degrees. Thus, its value is always half of either the outside diameter (for the pentagon, heptagon or circle) or the inside diameter (for the square, hexagon, octagon or dodecagon). Figure 7-3 lists the normalized stress levels for each of the configurations, with a value of 1.0 assigned to the configuration with the lowest stress level. The stress level is lowest in the square and highest in the pentagon and the heptagon. Keep in mind that this is an indicator of the maximum stress level when the rod is subjected to bending in the 0-180-degree plane. If the bending plane is rotated to some other angle, as often happens when fish fighting, the results would have been quite different. In fact, if the square rod were rotated 45 degrees (so that its maximum stress occurred at an outer corner), its maximum stress would be 42% higher.

And so, is there any one cross-section that is technically superior to the others? Surprisingly, the square configuration comes out best from the viewpoints of lightest weight, lowest aerodynamic profile and lowest stress level. To be perfectly candid, I thought that the circle would fare better. This brings forward some interesting questions. First, why did early rod makers go to such great lengths to shave their multi-splined rod sections down to approach a circular cross-section. Is it just because they didn't understand this technology or is it because they were simply trying to get back to the circular shapes common with the older, all-wood fly rods? And why did industry generally choose the hexagonal shape for the cane rod; especially when the square rod requires fewer pieces (splines) and fewer glue-lines? Was the hexagonal shape preferred because it gave the rod maker more choices (flats) for line guide location? Or was the square shape not popular because of the mistaken view that the corners caused a spine or stiffness instability? Or because they knew about the extremely high stresses associated with off-angle bending? Maybe our fly-fishing historians will get some answers to these questions as they continue to uncover the remnants of our past.

Rod Blank Spine

When a fly rod is perfectly made, it has no spine; i.e. it will resist bending equally in all planes. Figure 7-4 depicts a graphite fly rod cross-section; assume that it is perfectly symmetrical throughout its length except for the attachment of a small semicircular steel rod at the zero-degree position along the full length of the rod. When subjected to bending around axis X-X, the additional area of the steel attachment stiffens the rod selectively in plane Y-Y. This stiffening occurs whether the steel is on the outside or the inside of the bending curvature, because the steel provides resistance equally in tension or compression.

The problem with this selective stiffening is that it is basically unstable. Unless the fly rod is restrained from twisting throughout its length, the rod will tend to flop over to its orientation of least resistance; i.e. so that the steel moves to either the 90- or the 270-degree position, the neutral axis of bending. If an angler is casting the fly rod of Figure 7-4, even the most careful attention to the casting stroke will not prevent the tip from twisting, since it is not restrained from torsion or twisting like the butt section under the angler's hand. Since fly-casting involves repetitive, reversing flexure, the rod tip oscillates from side to side during the forward and rearward casting strokes as the tip twists and untwists. This oscillation hurts both casting distance and accuracy, since the fly line unfailingly follows the rod tip motion. The extent of this oscillation is directly proportional to the degree of non-symmetrical stiffening.

Of course, typical fly rods aren't generally stiffened with steel ribs, nor are their spines quite as obvious or severe. In fact, some of today's highest-quality fly rods barely exhibit a trace of spine. When a spine is present, it is usually due to one or a combination of the factors depicted on Figure 7-5. Each of these factors or non-symmetries are shown on Figure 7-5 in greatly exaggerated form and are depicted so that the stiffening occurs at the zero-degree position. Accordingly, under significant bending each of these non-symmetries will tend to flop the rod 90 degrees to either the right or left. Each of these are briefly described below:

Eccentricity: The circular outside diameter has shifted relative to the mandrel centerline. Even though the fiber content remains relatively equal around the mandrel, the shifted circular area has altered the shape's moment of inertia characteristics.

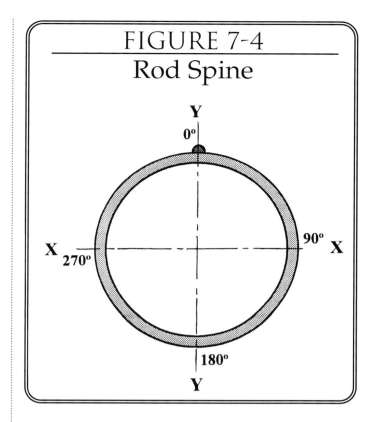

FIGURE 7-4
Rod Spine

Ovality: The outside diameter has departed from a circular shape, probably due to incomplete shrink tape compaction. The cross-section's moment of inertia becomes very non-symmetrical.

Thin-Wall Area: The exterior has been somehow flattened during curing. Again, fiber content around the mandrel is unchanged, but the symmetry of the moment of inertia in the X-X plane has been severely compromised.

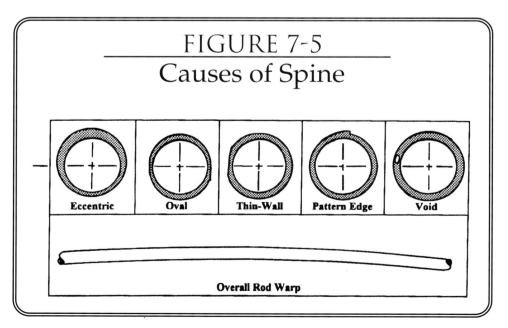

FIGURE 7-5
Causes of Spine

Eccentric   Oval   Thin-Wall   Pattern Edge   Void

Overall Rod Warp

Pattern Edge Ridge: Incomplete composite compaction has prevented the prepreg pattern edge from being squeezed into the circular shape. This causes the opposite effect of the thin-wall section, by locally increasing the moment of inertia in the 0-180-degree plane.

Void Inclusion: Insufficient compaction has permitted a gas bubble to form during curing. This reduces the local moment of inertia, particularly if the bubble is near the outer surface.

Overall Rod Warp: If the fly-rod blank cures with significant internal residual stresses, warping will result, which cannot be safely straightened unless the resin is of the thermoplastic type. This defect tends to mask all sources for spine, with the bending curve almost always following the warping direction.

Other sources of spine, not shown on Figure 7-5, include areas of fiber-resin de-bonding, resin-rich areas and areas of high-fiber concentration. All of these other sources affect local stiffness by changing the local material modulus of elasticity, not the moment of inertia.

It should be kept in mind that some or all of the above sources of spine could be present at one or many locations along the length of the rod. What's important to the rod maker and fly-fisher is the "effective" spine, or the integrated result of all such non-symmetries, to the extent that they affect casting or even fish-fighting. The term "effective spine" was first coined by the national organization, RodCrafters, several years ago in order to provide a common term for a characteristic often considered by rod builders when locating line guides. Fly-rod builders usually locate the line guides so that normal casting and fish-fighting is not compromised by unwanted lateral or twisting forces. Using various techniques, rod sections or assembled rods are simultaneously flexed and rotated to find the orientation which provides the greatest flexure for any given bending moment. This ensures that the rod won't twist during casting, since the most flexible plane is the most stable condition. For the configurations shown on Figure 7-5, this would mean that the line guides should be located at either 90 or 270 degrees.

Some fly rods also exhibit a secondary spine, where flexure in the 90-degree and 270-degree directions are not the same. Although I haven't conducted any detailed experiments of this phenomenon, I believe I know the reason for its existence. The modulus of elasticity of steel, boron and many other materials are very nearly equal in both the tensile and the compressive modes of loading. Graphite, on the other hand has a tensile modulus of elasticity which is considerably higher than its compressive modulus of elasticity. Accordingly, a local stiffening under tension will be much more apparent than its stiffening under compression.

Some rod builders prefer to locate the line guides so that the stiffer side is working during the forward delivery cast. Personally, I like to have nearly the same rod flexure on both the forward cast and the back cast. If this is not the case, I'd find myself another fly rod.

Chapter 8
COMPONENT DESIGN

Alarge portion of this book is being devoted to the primary rod structure, the blank, and how it works. The rod's behavior as a vibrating structure is particularly important, since so little of substance has been written on this subject over the years. Nevertheless, the rod's hardware or components can have a significant effect on rod performance, and the purpose of this chapter is to discuss these effects.

Ferrule Design

The need to disassemble a fly rod into shorter sections for ease of handling and transportation has been with us for well over two centuries. Very old fly rods also needed some type of ferrule to provide a connection between dissimilar materials; a situation which might even become more prevalent in the future. Technically, the old spliced joints were actually the best configuration, except that they worked well in only one casting plane and were cumbersome to assemble and disassemble. Their principal attribute was that they required no additional material for joining and load transfer.

The convenience of friction-fit ferrules is undeniable, and nickel-silver, fiberglass and graphite ferrules have all enjoyed considerable use and popularity. The difficult design challenges have been to provide a secure, reliable and lasting joint which won't add too much weight and which won't unduly affect the smooth flexure of the fly rod. Mid-ferrules on two-piece rods and butt ferrules on three-piece rods do not represent a particularly difficult design challenge because the added weight is not located very far from the angler's hand (little effect on his torque requirements) and because the local stiffness increases are relatively modest. Not so however with the tip ferrules for 3-, 4- and 5-piece fly rods. These ferrules require extreme attention to minimize weight and stiffness increases to make sure that the fly rod's casting performance is not impaired. Chapter 9 will discuss the effect of weight and stiffness on casting in more detail, but for now let's just say that the ideal ferrule is one which has no additional weight or stiffness beyond that in the equivalent one-piece rod.

Figure 8-1 provides some quantitative insight into the problems of ferrule design. Shown are three different configurations of nickel-silver ferrules which have been used on cane fly rods, and a macro-look at the stiffness profiles for each. For baseline purposes, I again used a nominal cane section stiffness of 500 pound-inches squared, typical of what might be found at the midpoint of an 8-foot, 6-weight fly rod. All three configurations assume a hexagonal cane cross-section having a maximum (corner-to-corner) diameter of 14/64 inches and a minimum (flat-to-flat) diameter of 12/64 inches. Both tip and butt cane sections have

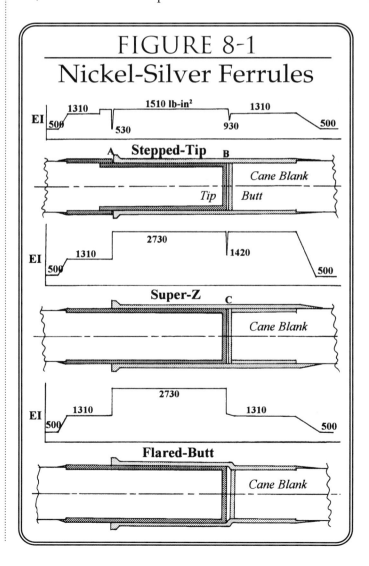

FIGURE 8-1
Nickel-Silver Ferrules

FIGURE 8-2
Ferrule Materials – Past and Present

Properties Material	Modulus of Elasticity - psi	Ultimate Tensile Strength - psi	Density - lbs/cubic inch
Aluminum	10 million	80,000	0.098
Brass	15 million	90,000	0.310
Nickel-Silver	18 million	110,000	0.315
Steel	30 million	250,000	0.285
*S-Glass/Epoxy	6 million	325,000	0.065
*Hi-Str.Graphite/Epoxy	20 million	380,000	0.053
*Boron/Epoxy	28 million	250,000	0.073
*Kevlar™/Epoxy	9.5 million	200,000	0.050

* Unidirectional, 50% Volume Fraction

been reduced in diameter for a short distance, to allow assembly of standard 12/64-inch inside diameter nickel-silver tubing.

The first configuration uses a step-down male ferrule with an engagement diameter of 12/64 inches. This very popular design exhibits a maximum stiffness (EI) level of 1510 pound-inches squared, or about three times the cane section stiffness of 500 pound-inches squared. This is a rather significant local increase in rod stiffening, in spite of its rather streamlined appearance. The reasons for this substantial stiffening are the larger diameter of the female ferrule and the 18 million psi modulus of elasticity for the drawn, nickel-silver material. This local rod stiffening is partially mitigated by the relatively "soft" areas at A and B. These transition areas temporarily reduce the stiffness level to 530 and 930 pound-inches squared, respectively, giving this ferrule the equivalent of two internal "hinges" at A and B. Note that these hinges are not particularly significant, provided that the local stiffness levels are not less than the cane rod stiffness levels on either side of the ferrule. These areas are however locations of high stress concentration.

I was intimately exposed to this hinging at area A while I was developing my earliest boron fly rods, because I used this ferrule design. With a solid boron/epoxy rod underneath, the nickel-silver step-down ferrule became the weak link in the system, and many of these ferrules broke at point A under strenuous service. I then changed to the Super-Z design, described in the next paragraph.

The Super-Z ferrule is a very clean and uncomplicated design, but as you can see from the EI or stiffness curve, it raises the stiffness level up to 2730 pound-inches squared, nearly five-and-one-half times the stiffness of the cane rod section. This design however also has an internal hinge, at area C, where the tip ferrule approaches the barrier wall of the female ferrule, reducing the stiffness locally to a level of 1420 pound-inches squared. This ferrule was also unsatisfactory for my boron fly rods; no failures were experienced, but many of my female ferrules were bent or deformed during use. I finally solved this problem by adding another layer of nickel-silver tubing over the female ferrule. Since the boron/epoxy material modulus of elasticity is about 27 million psi, much more than the 18 million psi for nickel-silver, this did not create any problems of excessive local stiffening. The additional weight however prevented me from producing any successful 3- or 4-piece fly rods.

The flared-butt ferrule design depicted on Figure 8-1 has some improvements over the Super-Z ferrules because of the shorter section exhibiting the maximum EI of 2730 pound-inches squared. It also provides considerable weight saving, though at the expense of some manufacturing complexity. In summary, though, I believe that the popularity of the stepped-down tip ferrule design is well-deserved for cane fly rods.

Although the nickel-silver ferrule has served the cane fly rod industry well over the years, its weight and cost has prevented its general adoption by the fiberglass and graphite fly rod manufacturers. The weight factor has been particularly significant due to the market appeal of multi-piece fly rods. Other metal ferrules have been used with varying degrees of success, but they also haven't found many applications in fiberglass and graphite fly rods. The data of Figure 8-2 helps to explain why. The densities of all of these metals except aluminum are much greater than the densities of resin composites containing either fiberglass or graphite. Aluminum, however, has very little self-lubricating ability (needed for a friction-fit ferrule) and has been used successfully for ferrules only by employing elastomer O-rings for friction control. It's unfortunate that their weight and/or cost is prohibitive,

since their modulii of elasticity generally provide a good match to the modern graphite fly rod.

Fortunately, the inherent characteristics of fiberglass and graphite composite materials provides an excellent and in fact superior alternative to metal ferrules. The ability to match blank and ferrule material modulus of elasticity is obvious. Even more important however is the ability to tailor the orientation of the high-performance fibers in the helical and longitudinal directions, so that there is just enough material to satisfy the local stresses. For example, refer to Figure 8-3, which shows two typical graphite ferrule designs and their respective stiffness profiles relative to a nominal rod section stiffness of 500 pound-inches squared. These designs and their component modulii of elasticity have been based upon typical graphite/resin construction, with most of the fibers oriented longitudinally, in the direction of the fly rod centerline.

Note areas A of the sleeve ferrule and spigot ferrule designs. These are the areas of engagement for the male and female ferrule halves. In both designs, very few longitudinal fibers are needed,

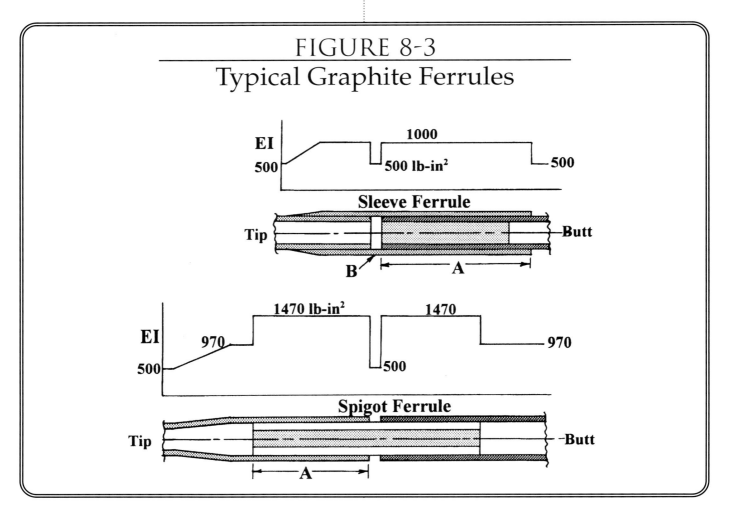

FIGURE 8-3
Typical Graphite Ferrules

because there is more than enough section stiffness in the underlying male ferrule to provide adequate resistance to bending. What is needed in these areas are primarily sufficient helical fiber windings to maintain ferrule circularity to prevent separation of the ferrule halves. Note however that the sleeve ferrule does require a full complement of longitudinal fibers at area B, to prevent an otherwise disastrous point of weakness. The main point to be made with regard to Figure 8-3 is that my calculated maximum stiffness levels of 1000 and 1470 pound-inches squared for the sleeve and spigot ferrules respectively can be significantly reduced via careful engineering design. Accordingly, weight reductions can be accomplished, together with a smoother flexural profile.

Another facet of ferrule design that deserves some discussion is engagement length, the length of the ferrule section where the male and female halves are engaged in a friction fit. Because of the inevitable local increase in section stiffness, it's desirable to minimize engagement length and thus minimize the so-called "flat-spot" that inhibits a smooth flexural profile. If engagement length is shortened too much, however, there will be insufficient ferrule friction to prevent the male and female halves from working apart during normal use. For nickel-silver ferrules on cane rods, engagement lengths in the range of one-half to three-quarters of an inch are quite satisfactory because of the extremely close fits (high-friction) achievable and the resultant vacuum forces that help to prevent ferrule separation. In comparison, graphite ferrules must have a longer engagement length for equivalent friction levels, since the graphite/graphite interface is relatively soft and slippery. Unlike the nickel-silver ferrule, the modern graphite ferrule incorporates a very shallow diametral taper, not unlike the Morse tapers used in machine tools for accessory attachment and removal. This taper is absolutely necessary to maintain sufficient friction, since the graphite surfaces will wear. Modest, even wearing is not a real problem; the only effect is a very slightly shorter rod length. If the graphite ferrules were constant-diameter, this wear would rapidly result in a sloppy ferrule fit and loss of friction forces.

Line Guides

Although making up only a very small fraction of the weight and volume of the assembled fly rod, line guides are of critical importance to the casting and fish-fighting performance of the fly rod. The most obvious function of the guides is to channel the line while shooting it during the delivery cast. For maximum line speed and control, the path of the line during shooting should be relatively smooth and with a minimum of sharp corners or turns. Anytime the line path changes direction, inertial effects introduce lateral line motion and guide friction losses which reduce casting efficiency. Although a very smooth line shooting path could be created by attaching a tapered tube to the fly rod, the tube's internal surface would collectively cause sufficient friction to more than negate any benefits of a smoothly-curved shooting path. As a compromise, a relatively large number of line guides are used, to minimize the extent of line path direction changes at any one guide.

Guide spacing is really a compromise between what provides the best line shoot and what best distributes rod stress during casting and fish-fighting. Over the years, the fly-rod manufacturers have adopted remarkably similar guide spacing patterns. Most of today's better fly rods incorporate a tip-top guide plus additional line guides equal to the length of the fly rod, in feet, plus one. Thus, a typical nine-foot fly rod would incorporate a tip-top plus ten line guides. Generally, the first line guide is located 4-5 inches from the tip-top, and each successive guide is spaced a little further from its neighbor. The final or lower line guide is usually located 28 to 36 inches from the rod's butt end. The specific location of the lower line guide is very important and can vary considerably, depending on the fly-fisher and his casting style. Here again, the objective is to make sure that the path of the shooting line between the fly-fisher's line hand and the guides is as smooth as practical. Figure 8-4 depicts some typical guide spacings for fly rod lengths varying between six and nine feet. Please note however that these are just typical, and not necessarily optimum for any given angler or rod design.

Recently, while discussing fly rod line guides with my friend and neighbor Dale Clemens (noted author and master rod builder), Dale mentioned that several acquaintances have reported improved line shooting distance by installing an additional line guide just a few inches up from the lower guide. Although at first this sounded rather strange, further analysis of the geometry of this situation tends to support this contention. Figure 8-5 (page 74) is a drawing showing the relative location of my hands, the grip and the first two guides of one of my favorite rods used for snook and redfish. The solid line ABC represents the stationary line position, as when fighting a fish or at the end of the forward casting stroke, just before the line

FIGURE 8-4
Typical Fly Rod Guide Spacing

Rod Length / Guide No.	Guide Location - Inches From the Tip-Top						
	6 Ft.	6-1/2 Ft.	7 Ft.	7-1/2 Ft.	8 Ft.	8-½ Ft.	9 Ft.
1	4-1/2	4-1/2	4-1/2	4-3/8	5-1/8	5-5/8	5
2	9-1/4	9-3/4	10-1/4	9-3/4	10-1/2	11-5/8	10-1/2
3	15-1/4	16	16-1/2	15-5/8	16	18-1/4	16-1/4
4	22-1/8	23-1/2	23	21-5/8	22	25-1/4	22-3/8
5	30-1/4	32	30-1/4	28	28-1/4	32-5/8	28-1/2
6	39-1/4	41	37-1/2	34-7/8	35-1/2	40-1/4	35
7	48-1/4	50	46-1/4	42-1/2	44	48-3/8	41-3/4
8			55-1/2	51	55-7/8	57	49
9				61-1/2	67-1/4	65-3/4	58
10						74-3/4	66-5/8
11							78-1/2

shoot. The angle ABC is approximately 120 degrees. During casting, at the point when the line begins to shoot, I release my finger grip on the line, instead making an "O" with my thumb and middle finger to guide the line path toward the lower line guide. With high line shooting speeds, the line no longer follows the path ABC around the corner at the lower line guide. Instead, its momentum and inertia will carry the line along the path ABDEC or something similar, as it wends its way through the guides and out the tip-top. The extent to which the line path wanders outside the ideal (frictionless) path depends upon line speed, line density and whether or not the line speed is constant, accelerating or decelerating.

Consider also that continuation of the path ABDEC may involve some cyclical lateral wandering, before settling down into a straight line shoot. I'm sure that many readers have heard and indeed felt the "chatter" as this lateral instability is damped out via impact with the line guides (it's very similar to the noise produced when casting in very cold

conditions where the line retains its coiled shape in spite of repeated attempts at stretching). The amplitude and persistence of lateral line instability should be largely dependent upon the amount of initial wandering near points D and E. Accordingly, the addition of another line guide might go a long way toward minimizing aerodynamic, inertial and friction losses during casting, even though the line's initial contact will most certainly involve some frictional losses. Now, I hasten to add that at this point this is just a theory on my part. Some rigorous experimentation is needed to determine whether this is indeed the reason why the additional guide produces longer line shoots. If so, this suggests that other, more sophisticated line gathering devices may be quite effective in improving line shooting distance. At any rate, the weight of the additional guide shouldn't create any problems because it's located relatively close to the angler's hand and would thus require very little additional casting torque. Another issue raised by Figure 8-5 is whether or not we fly-fishers can improve our line-

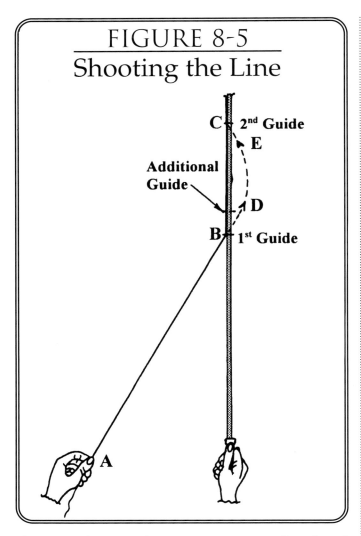

FIGURE 8-5
Shooting the Line

C — 2nd Guide

E

Additional
Guide

D

B — 1st Guide

A

shooting distance by positioning our line hand closer to the rod grip to change the angle formed by ABC. Although it would at first feel somewhat awkward, this merits further study and consideration.

Another important aspect of line guide design is the weight of the guide. Any concentrated weight, especially near the end of the rod tip, will add to the energy requirements of the caster. More important however is the effect that the additional weight will have on the dynamics of the cast. The heavier the guide, the more difficult it will be to achieve high line speeds without getting tip bounce and other distance-robbing effects. Of course, it should be kept in mind that the importance of line guide weight is not just dependent upon its distance from the angler's hand. A relatively stiff-tipped fly rod can tolerate heavier line guides without introducing casting problems. It should also be kept in mind that the weight of the guide is just part of the story. The weight of the guide windings and the preservative and coatings on the windings also add to the weight and the potential for casting problems.

The importance of guide weight has been obvi-

ous for over a century; accordingly, fine-wire, snake-type guides have been standard on quality fly rods. Some might say that the persistence of snake guides is an issue of tradition, but I doubt it. A miniature (size 4/0) chrome-plated stainless steel snake guide weighs about 0.8 grains. That's 0.00183 ounces! By comparison, even a single-foot ceramic guide with an equivalent opening size weighs about 3.8 grains, nearly 4 times heavier. Equivalent double-foot ceramic guides will weigh close to 5 grains. Based on weight only, the conventional snake guide and its nearest competitor, the single-foot wire guide, are clearly the best choice, especially for long, flexible-tipped rods for light lines. It's surprising that more improvements haven't been made in tip-tops over the years, in view of their location and contribution to rod weight. I recently weighed a number of conventional, tube-type tip-tops on a reloading scale. The results are shown on the following table:

Tip-Top Tube I.D.	3/64	4/64	4.5/64	5/64	5.5/64
Weight - Grains	3.5	7.6	8.0	8.0	8.4

The above information shows that typical tip-tops weigh much more than their companion snake guides. This is unfortunate, since there are certainly many opportunities for lighter-weight design alternatives. I recall using a re-bent snake guide as a tip-top, before I could get delivery on some special-order size 3 tip-tops for my 2- and 3-weight fly rods. The snake guide feet were reoriented to point in the same direction and were shortened and ground to very narrow and thin dimensions. These feet were positioned to straddle the sides of the rod tip, and were held in place with epoxy and thread wraps. Although requiring additional weight of epoxy and thread, these makeshift tip-tops were nevertheless only 23% of the weight of even the special, size 3 tip-tops that were and are the lightest available in the industry.

Another aspect of tip-tops worth mentioning is that the common pear-shaped design necks down to a v-shape before entering its containing tube. Often, this v-shape is shallow enough to pinch the fly line during line shoot, creating additional friction and reducing shooting distance. Although the line tends to rub against the outer, more circular portion of the tip-top, the line will often move laterally and get into this v-section. The easiest way to correct this problem is to bend the v-section to open it up and/or to fill it in with a hard epoxy.

For the lower, stripping guides close to the angler's hand, double-foot guides are fairly standard. Early fly rods incorporated stripping guides with brazed tungsten-carbide rings that might weigh as much as 25 to 35 grains. Although some of these types of stripping guides are still used on quality cane fly rods, nearly all modern graphite rods incorporate stripping guides with aluminum oxide or silicon carbide rings that weigh close to half of the older types. Today's decided preference for ceramic or cermet stripping guides has been largely fueled by their high wear resistance and low coefficient of friction. The latter property minimizes line/guide friction to facilitate line shooting and both properties act to minimize line wear. Line wear is most important at the stripping guide and at the tip-top, where fish-fighting line loads can exert considerable lateral pressure on the guide rings.

Over the past ten years there has been considerable discussion on the effect of guide opening size on the casting performance of a fly rod using heavier line weights. An accepted strategy for sizing guides on spinning rods is to lay out a sketch of a tapered cone whose point coincides with the center of the rod's tip-top and whose base diameter coincides with the outer diameter of the open-faced spinning reel. If the spinning guides are located and sized so that their guide ring inner diameters line up with the cone's outer surface, friction should be minimized and casting distance should be at a maximum. Although the spinning rod analogy can't fully apply to the fly rod because of the offset location of the line source (the angler's line hand), the general concept of a conical guide ring diametral profile seems appropriate. This is of course also supported by the need to reduce guide weight as its location nears the rod tip.

The fundamental question is, however, whether line guide size is really important. For a perspective on this issue, please refer to Figure 8-6, which comparatively shows the opening size of a size 2/0 snake guide (0.188 inches) and the cross-section diameter of the belly of a WF-6F fly line (0.047 inches). I have designed and tested many 6-weight fly rods using size 2/0 and 3/0 snake guides and, to the best of my knowledge, have never had a problem of losing line-shooting distance. Figure 8-6 shows that when the line rubs against the wire guide, the area of contact or friction is very small. And, if the guide opening size were to be either reduced to that of a 4/0 guide (shown dotted), or if the line size were increased to a WF8F (also shown dotted), the resultant area of actual contact is not appreciably affected. I conclude, therefore, that the ratio of line guide inside diameter and line diameter is, within reasonable limits, unimportant to line

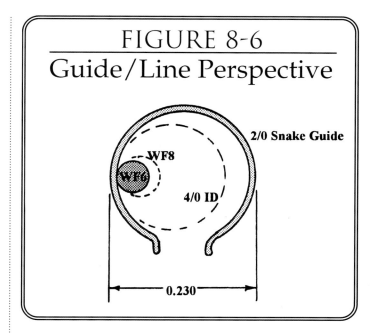

FIGURE 8-6
Guide/Line Perspective

shooting performance. Accordingly, if larger line guide size is indeed important to shooting performance, its importance must be due to its greater tolerance for knots or lateral motion without contact. There are certainly some opportunities for experimentation here. Controlled line-shooting experiments with differing line guide sizes and guide/line friction (noise) measurements should produce some interesting results.

Another variable associated with the design of line guides is the standoff height or the distance between the rod surface and the centerline of the guide opening. This of course only applies to guides with full ring inserts; snake guides are nearly semicircular in profile and provide no support for preventing line/rod contact. Greater standoff heights do add weight to the guide, so they should not be adopted without good justification. One often-stated justification is to keep the line away from the rod so that it won't make contact during line shooting. My studies indicate that this concern is somewhat overstated. During most of the back cast, the line doesn't rub against the rod blank because the rod orientation causes the line to rub against the outer portion of the guide wire. During the forward delivery cast, the line can indeed rub against the rod during the early stages of the casting stroke. In fact, the line rests in intimate contact with the rod where snake guides are used. Stop-action video images of casting have however shown me that the line doesn't even begin to move or shoot until the rod has nearly straightened. And as line shooting continues, the fly rod curves somewhat forward, lifting the line from any rod contact. Accordingly, if standoff height is indeed important to line shooting, this importance must be due to other factors such as the ability to keep lateral line oscillations from slapping the rod surface.

A final aspect of line guides worth discussing is the effect of the guide stiffness on the stiffness of the rod blank. I haven't performed any real testing on this subject, but my intuitive feeling is that this is not a particularly important issue except for the uppermost two or three guides on rods for very light lines (0-, 1- and 2-weight). If one holds a loose, small snake guide between the thumb and forefingers of both hands, it's easy to verify that the over-

all guide flexes quite easily, without much effort. It is certainly nowhere near the stiffness level of an equal length of rod tip. On the other hand, the stiffness of each guide foot is significant, but only for a relatively short distance. Even significant stiffness increases are not particularly important if concentrated within short lengths. Keep in mind that the guide wraps and epoxy play essentially no role in this matter, since the helical thread orientation has no stiffness in the longitudinal direction. The newer, single-foot wire guides have only one foot adding stiffness to the rod blank, but this foot incorporates two wire lengths which should have

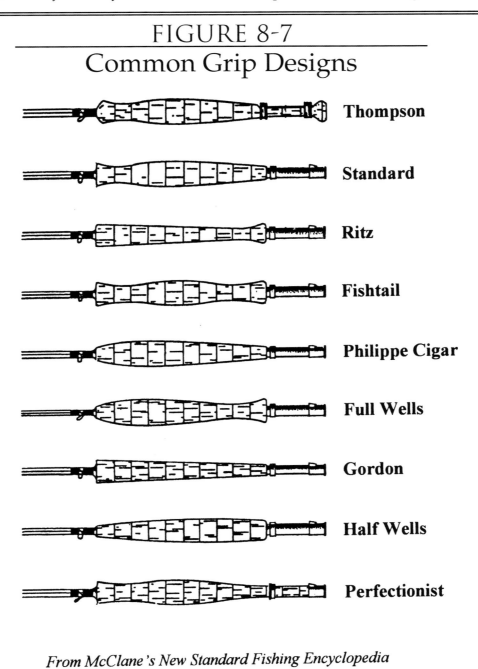

FIGURE 8-7
Common Grip Designs

Thompson

Standard

Ritz

Fishtail

Philippe Cigar

Full Wells

Gordon

Half Wells

Perfectionist

From McClane's New Standard Fishing Encyclopedia

roughly the same effect as the two, single-wire feet. The lower or stripping guides will of course be much stiffer than the tip's uppermost snake guides, but their stiffness can be totally ignored because of the very high local rod stiffness levels.

In order to resolve any questions about line guide stiffness effects, it's best to simply check the assembled rod to see if any problems have surfaced. There are two simple tests which can determine whether or not the addition of guides will have a negative effect on rod performance. First, re-check the rod spine in the usual way. If it has moved so that it is now not in the 90/270-degree plane, a casting instability has been introduced. Another test is to lightly clamp the rod at the grip, with the guides located underneath, in the 180 degree position. Then, grab the rod tip, deflect it downward a significant amount, and release it. If the rod oscillation remains in the 0/180-degree plane while vibrating, the rod's spine has not been appreciably affected. If either of these tests uncovers a problem, the desired spine location can probably be restored by removing the guides and liberally grinding the guide feet.

Fly-Rod Grips

Fly-rod grips come in many different shapes, as shown on Figure 8-7, reproduced from McClane's "New Standard Fishing Encyclopedia." The main requirement for the grip is for it to be comfortable to the angler under a broad variety of fishing conditions. The large variety of popular shapes suggests that there is little agreement as to what's most comfortable, and that this is largely a matter of personal preference. Many fly-fishers, including yours truly, prefer those grips having larger diameters under the thumb of the casting hand when longer casts are required. Figure 8-8 shows the reason for this preference. The smaller, upper diameters require a longer thumb extension to obtain solid contact with the grip. Also, the angle between the cork surface and the thumb joint is rather shallow, requiring a tighter overall grip to prevent the thumb from slipping during long casts. I find both of these requirements to be somewhat uncomfortable.

Overall, grip diameter is dependent upon the size of the fly-fisher's hand and his or her gripping preferences. The generally smaller hands of lady fly-fishers usually require smaller diameters. Some anglers prefer the feel of a larger grip and others like smaller diameters. A lot depends on the type of grasp employed and the degree of flexibility desired between the hand and the rod grip. Custom-shaped grips are favored

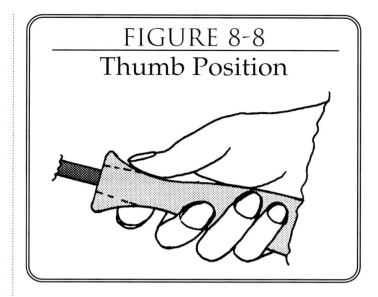

FIGURE 8-8
Thumb Position

by some fly-fishers, in order to fit their hand with equal pressure and thus gain the utmost in comfort. Such customization may be appropriate for some people, but this reduces the rod's value for resale. Also, a custom fit is usually unique to a particular grip position, creating problems if the angler should wish to alter his grip position from time to time. I tend to keep my grip in the same position while fly-fishing, except when fighting a heavy fish. Then, I rotate my thumb to the left side of the grip (I'm right-handed), move my hand to the extreme front-end of the grip and position the rod butt under my forearm for additional leverage.

For many years, specie cork has been the grip material of choice for fly-fishers. Cork is very light, and yet it has enough rigidity (called bulk modulus by the technical community) to transmit the forces of the angler's hand to the rod blank without too much attenuation or loss of response. Cork feels comfortable in the hand, and doesn't feel particularly cold even under near-freezing conditions. Manufactured foam grips are very popular for some other types of fishing rods, but fly-fishers have generally found them too soft and unresponsive to the pressures of the angler's hand. As Schwiebert points out in Table A-3, Reference No. 17, the thumb and each finger of the rod hand play a definitive role at various stages of the fly-cast. With an exceptionally-soft grip material the more subtle of these motions are rendered less-effective. I suspect, however, that we haven't heard the last of foam grips for fly rods. The technology to produce lightweight foam materials with higher bulk modulus may not be that far away. Also, Doug Swisher has been experimenting with reduced-diameter cork grips, with vinyl wraps glued over the cork. The wraps are made of the same material used in both golf club and tennis racquet grips. The resultant fly-rod grips have a very pleasant feel to them, and the underlying cork provides enough bulk modulus to guarantee a responsive feeling during casting. The easy replaceability of the vinyl wraps is another good feature of this innovation.

Butt extension grips can be an important feature on fly rods used for fighting exceptionally large or strong fish, because of the additional leverage to be gained by the angler. Unfortunately, this additional length creates more inertia that the angler must deal with while casting. Removable butt extensions solve the casting problem, but these are often misplaced or hard to find during the heat of battle. Fore grips are another method of gaining additional leverage during fish fighting. These should not be used however unless the rod manufacturer has designed the blank for their use. Often, I'll place my left hand on the upper end of the butt section when fish-fighting, just to give my right wrist a little relief. However, having a fore grip is an invitation to grab it and really put some pressure on a fish. If the rod is not designed to have a fulcrum at this point, over-stressing and failure may result.

Reel Seats

As was noted in Chapter 2, there have been countless ways that fly-fishers have used to attach a reel to the fly rod. Currently, fly-reel seats are usually of the screw-lock or slide band type. The latter are usually reserved for light-line freshwater rods, where there is less likelihood of the reel coming loose during normal use. If slide bands do loosen, it is generally because of two problems. First, some reel feet are relatively thick and have a relatively steep angle on which the slide band rests. It often doesn't take much jostling for the band to slip just a fraction of an inch, and this significantly lowers its holding pressure and invites further slipping. A highly-flexible slide band helps to minimize this slipping. Another cause for reel loosening is when the underlying cork compresses with time and loses some of its natural resiliency. Usually, this can be at least partially corrected by steaming the grip to restore much of its original shape.

Some fly-fishers prefer the look of wood in their slide-band reel seats. Unfortunately, this eliminates the springy resiliency of cork needed for retention of slide band pressure on the reel seat. I solved this problem back in the 1970s by designing a split-reel seat, shown in Figure 8-9. Initially, an integral cork reel seat and grip was constructed. Then, a cork section was cut out and replaced with a glued-in slab of rosewood. The reel seat was then turned to its final diameter. This slide-band design has the dual benefit of using cork for resilient pressure on the reel feet plus hardwood for providing a rigid connection between the reel feet and the rod blank.

Screw-lock reel seats rely on the friction of screw threads to maintain hood pressure on the reel foot. The likelihood of hood loosening is minimized by using low-pitch screw threads and dual knurled locking rings. Anodized or coated aluminum is usually used in the screw-lock reel seat components, although nickel-silver and titanium is common on custom and very expensive fly rods. Nickel-silver is used because of its jewelry-type appearance and because its natural lubricity and strength prevents jamming, a periodic problem with aluminum threads when they become distorted. Nickel-silver is however not suitable for saltwater applications because of its tendency to corrode in the salt environment. Although very expensive, titanium is finding increasing usage because of its extremely light weight, high strength and corrosion resistance. Skeleton screw-locking reel seats are also quite popular, combining the functionality of a locking seat and the attractiveness of an underlying, polished hardwood cylinder.

Both slide-band and screw-locking reel seats can either be down-locking or up-locking. In down-locking designs, one reel foot is inserted into a fixed hood located at the butt end of the rod and the other foot is engaged to either a sliding band or a sliding hood. With up-locking designs, the fixed hood is located under the cork grip. I find either design to be quite workable, although I lean toward the up-locking designs because they place the reel closer to my hand, minimizing casting torque requirements.

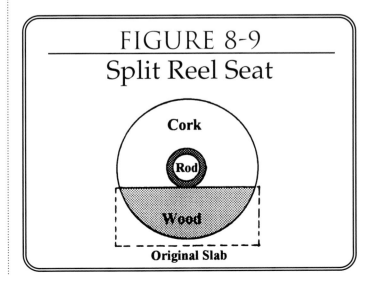

FIGURE 8-9
Split Reel Seat

Cork

Rod

Wood

Original Slab

Chapter 9
CASTING THE LINE AND FLY

Were it not for the art of fly-casting, i.e. the ability to accurately deliver a feathered hook a considerable distance, fly-fishing would be just another method of catching fish. The claim that fly-fishing is not just another fishing method is supported by many diverse facts. There are not many spin-fishing clubs. The literature of ice-fishing is relatively sparse. There are no certified trolling instructors. People seldom brag that they are bait-fishers. The craft of making surf plugs has not yet spawned its own bimonthly magazine. Fly-fishing is indeed special, and one of its unique aspects is the intimate and interactive relationship between the fly-caster and his fly rod. If not working together and in concert, the casting of the line and fly is arduous, awkward and ineffective. In contrast, a skilled fly-caster with a well-designed fly rod is pure poetry in motion, able to present the fly accurately with seemingly little effort. There is an intimate partnership between the angler and his fly rod; a curious mixture of art and science which has thus far defied attempts to reduce it to a systematic body of knowledge. Hopefully, this book and especially the following paragraphs will help to at least identify some of the important issues and point the way toward further needed studies.

Casting With and Without a Rod

One way of identifying the rod's function during casting is to take a look at hand-casting, casting of the line and fly without using a rod. Many fly-fishers have demonstrated the ability to do this. I can hand-cast about 30-40 feet and shoot 5 to 10 feet more, provided I move my hand very fast and in a fairly straight line. Figure 9-1 shows the mechanics of this scenario, assuming a range of hand motion of 3 feet, over a time interval of 1 second. The *average* hand/line speed is 3 feet/second. Since the starting and ending hand speed is 0 feet/second, the maximum

hand/line speed is much higher, perhaps two or three times the average speed. Although this is enough line speed to straighten a leader and shoot a few feet of line, it's not enough to meet most of fly-fishing's many and varied casting challenges. Now let's add a fly rod to this scenario, as shown in Figure 9-2 (following page). If we simply move the rod tip the same distance as the hand, we have not gained anything except the added burden of the weight of a fly rod.

However, If we simultaneously rotate the fly rod, as shown in Figure 9-3 (following page), we have more than doubled the rod tip travel distance over the same interval of time. With a 9-foot rod, this might typically result in an average rod tip/line speed of 6.6 feet/second. The problem with Figure 9-3 is that the rod shown is not flexed and the tip travels a somewhat circular path. As we know, this will direct the line downward, not acceptable under most casting situations. Of course, fly rods do bend; in fact they are designed to do so. If the rod's flexural characteristics are compatible with the angler's casting stroke, the mechanics of Figure 9-4 (following page) result, with the rod-tip traveling in a fairly straight line. Note that rod flex has not just

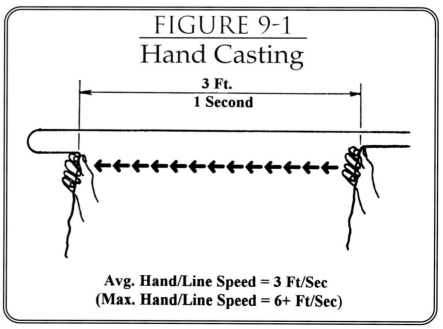

FIGURE 9-1
Hand Casting

3 Ft.
1 Second

Avg. Hand/Line Speed = 3 Ft/Sec
(Max. Hand/Line Speed = 6+ Ft/Sec)

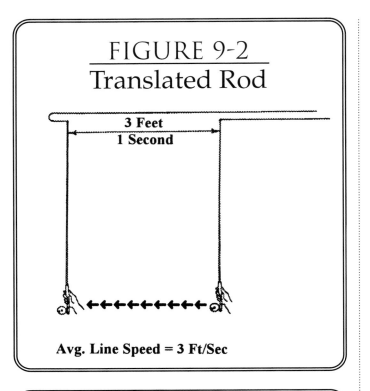

FIGURE 9-2
Translated Rod

3 Feet
1 Second

Avg. Line Speed = 3 Ft/Sec

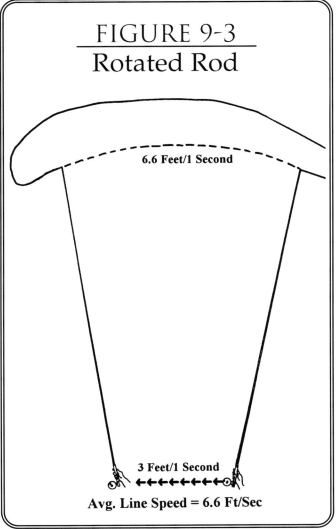

FIGURE 9-3
Rotated Rod

6.6 Feet/1 Second

3 Feet/1 Second

Avg. Line Speed = 6.6 Ft/Sec

straightened rod-tip travel. It has also lengthened rod-tip travel so that it is about 3 times the hand travel distance. Accordingly, by introducing a well-designed fly rod, a 9-foot flexible lever, we have been able to increase average rod tip and line speed to about 9 feet/second.

Figure 9-4 illustrates a 1 o'clock to 11 o'clock rod butt angular motion and a one-second casting stroke. This is probably typical of the casts required in many fishing situations. Often, though, there is the need for higher line speeds, to achieve greater casting distance or to compensate for cross-winds. Single- and double-hauling are techniques used to increase line speed, and they will be discussed later in this chapter. Another technique for increasing line speed is to increase hand speed by moving the hand over the same distance in a shorter time interval. Although this is intended to achieve higher maximum line speeds near the end of the casting stroke, this may in fact be difficult to implement without introducing distance-robbing tip bounce.

The most common method for increasing line speed is by increasing tip travel distance during the same casting stroke time interval. This is usually accomplished by both increasing the hand travel distance and increasing the angular motion of the rod butt. Figure 9-5 (following page) illustrates the mechanics of this cast, showing that the rod tip has now moved around 15 feet in one second, for an average line speed of 15 feet/second. Here, the additional tip travel distance is achieved by

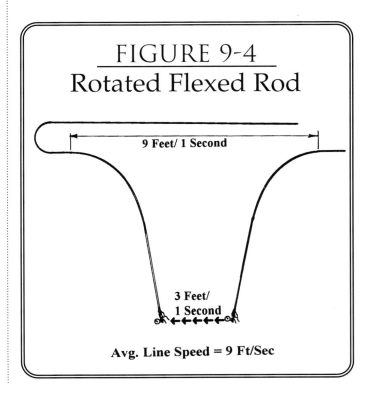

FIGURE 9-4
Rotated Flexed Rod

9 Feet/ 1 Second

3 Feet/
1 Second

Avg. Line Speed = 9 Ft/Sec

simultaneously: 1) moving the hand a greater distance, 2) extending the arm farther backward and forward and 3) using more wrist motion. Note that this has now changed the rod butt angular position so that the casting stroke moves between the 2 o'clock and the 10 o'clock positions. Actually, this approach can be carried much further, with added angler shoulder/body motions and with rod butt angles approaching the 3 o'clock and the 9 o'clock positions, further increasing line speeds if the angler has the skills to alter his casting stroke accordingly. With near-horizontal rod butt angles, the angler must change his hand-path from straight-line to concave (bowl-shaped), in order to maintain straight-line rod tip paths.

The Classical Fly-Cast

Fly-fishers practice their craft in the rivers, lakes, estuaries and beaches of the world. Casting styles vary widely from region to region and from angler to angler. There are dozens of specialty casts, each used to support some specific fly-fishing strategy. It is beyond the scope of this book to describe the many variations of casting styles and specialty casts; there are many fine and recent books and videos which describe these casts in extensive detail. Instead, I'll describe just the basic fly-fishing cast and only a few of its basic variations, but with considerable emphasis on the mechanics of the rod and line. As described in this section, the basic cast sequence consists of the pickup from a water surface, the back cast and the forward delivery cast. In the following paragraphs we will describe this sequence. To simplify the descriptive narrative, it will be assumed that the angler is right-handed, that the casting plane is perpendicular to the ground and that the angler's wrist/hand, the fly rod and the line loop stay within this casting plane.

To recover a completed cast, the angler points the rod directly at the fly, and uses the line hand to retrieve some line in one long pull. This gets the

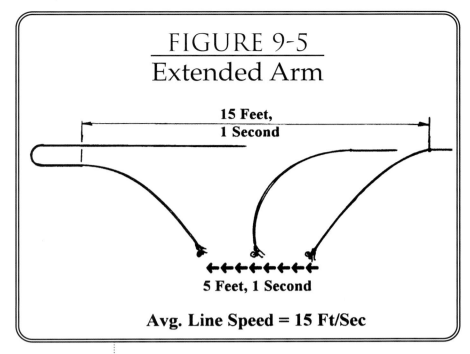

FIGURE 9-5
Extended Arm

15 Feet, 1 Second

5 Feet, 1 Second

Avg. Line Speed = 15 Ft/Sec

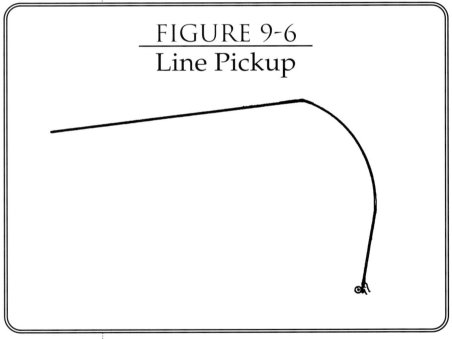

FIGURE 9-6
Line Pickup

line moving and breaks the water's surface tension forces (to simplify the casting process description, let's assume for now that the angler locks the line under his rod hand after the pull). While the line is still moving from the line hand pull, the angler rapidly draws the rod back and up, stopping suddenly at the 1 o'clock position. The angler's wrist remains in the adducted (cocked forward) position until the very end of this casting stroke. At the end of this stroke, the wrist is rapidly abducted (cocked backward), accelerating the rod tip and line to its maximum speed. Figure 9-6 depicts the rod and line at this point of maximum rod bend, when the

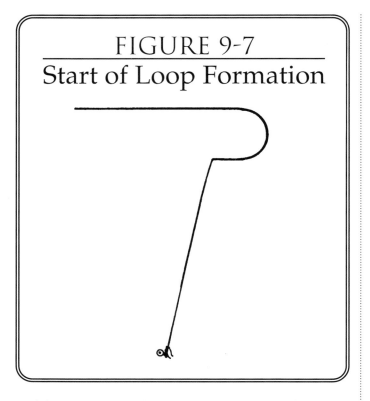

FIGURE 9-7
Start of Loop Formation

Once the angler stops the rod butt sharply at the approximately 1 o'clock position, the rod tip continues in the rearward direction until it has straightened and lost its potential energy. Once the tip is straight and relatively motionless, the line continues to move rearward and a line loop begins to form (see Figure 9-7). As the loop progresses rearward, an increasingly longer portion of the line is decelerated to zero. This line deceleration gradually bends the rod tip slightly in the rearward direction due to line inertial forces. Throughout the loop-forming process, aerodynamic drag forces are tending to reduce line speed, offsetting its kinetic energy. These aerodynamic drag forces are acting both longitudinally on the exterior of the moving line and laterally on the rolling loop, though the lateral drag forces are more dominant. In spite of the drag forces, the speed of the moving portion of the line remains relatively high since its kinetic energy is progressively transferred to an increasingly smaller length of line. Line and leader taper also promotes high line speeds because this kinetic energy transfers to an increasingly lower weight per foot of length.

At the instant that the line loop has fully unrolled, the line and leader are nearly motionless and essentially straight, as shown on Figure 9-8. At this time some anglers let the rod drift rearward, simultaneously raising their rod hand and rotating the rod back to the 2 or 3 o'clock position, to give the rod tip more forward travel distance for higher line speeds and greater shooting distances. For the classical cast, however, the rod tip is only slightly flexed to the rear, per Figure 9-8, storing potential energy as the line decelerates to zero speed. At this point, the angler begins his forward casting stroke,

rod butt is motionless and the line and fly have been lifted from the water surface. At this stage of the casting cycle, the line has kinetic energy defined by the equation K.E. = $\frac{1}{2}$ mv^2, where m equals the mass of the line and v equals the velocity or speed of the line. The line also has momentum, defined by the equation M = mv, which is a measure of the inertia of the line. In addition, since the rod is at its maximum flexed position it has stored potential energy within its structure. The determination of the amount of this potential energy is relatively complex and well beyond the scope of this book.

accelerating the rod grip. At first, the line and rod tip lag behind, further flexing the rod tip rearward due to the inertia of the rod tip and the line. Further acceleration of the rod butt puts additional bend in the upper rod, but as the rod stiffens it begins to increasingly accelerate the rod tip and line in the forward direction. During the latter stages of the angler's forward casting stroke his wrist is adducted forward, putting the maximum bend in the rod and simultaneously accelerating the rod tip and line to its maximum speed. The shape of the rod and line during this interval is shown on Figure 9-9 (following page).

FIGURE 9-8
End of Back Cast

The angler stops his casting stroke suddenly, causing the rod to bend forward, moving the rod tip from position 1 to position 2. The rod tip goes beyond its neutral or un-flexed position because of its inertia and because of the pull of the line as the forward loop forms and more and more of it decelerates to zero speed. Also, the angler may lower the rod somewhat to adjust loop size. You will remember that we assumed that the angler's rod hand kept the line tight against the rod grip. Although this is not usual, it's convenient for the purposes of this description to make sure that there is no movement of the line beyond the rod tip. Accordingly, this classical cast involves no line shoot; the line and leader loop continually unrolls, the line straightens and the fly alights on the water's surface.

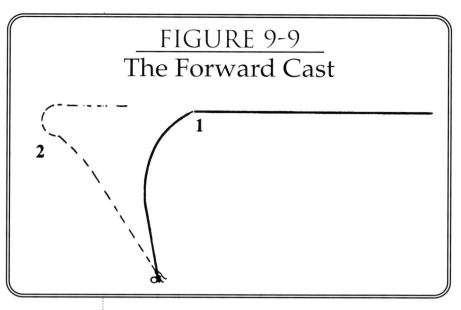

FIGURE 9-9
The Forward Cast

Usually, when an angler makes a forward delivery cast without line shoot he holds the line in his line hand throughout the unrolling of the line loop. The novice caster invariably holds the line hand in one rigid position while casting. Since the rod hand moves back and forth during casting, this means that the distance between the line hand and the lower stripping guide continually changes. As shown on Figure 9-10, during the back cast, rod hand motion from position 1 to position 2 creates an additional pull on the line which is helpful in accelerating the line for a good back cast. Conversely, during the forward stroke (when the angler's hand moves from position 2 to position 3) the distance between the line hand and the lower stripping guide is reduced, creating line slack instead of the line tension which is required for a controlled cast. The experienced fly-caster learns to move the line hand away from the rod hand, to eliminate line slack. When I initially instruct novice fly-casters, I encourage them to keep the line trapped between the rod hand and the rod grip, so that they can first learn the basic casting stroke without the complication of dealing with the left hand.

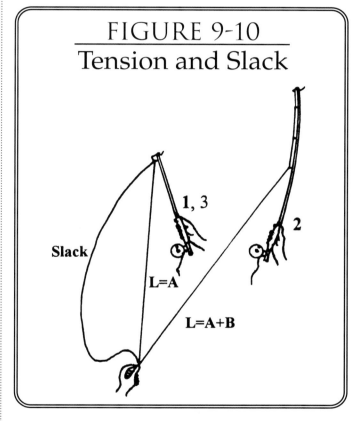

FIGURE 9-10
Tension and Slack

Shooting the Line
The classical fly-cast described in the preceding paragraphs is a basic fishing cast, one which might be used quite successfully working a stretch of trout stream in a repetitive fishing pattern while slowly working up or downstream. I have used this approach quite often when blind-fishing long runs of similar composition. Unfortunately, some anglers restrict their casting repertoire to only this cast, limiting their distance capability to the length of line that they can comfortably false cast. Also, there are times when false casting is necessary, to dry a fly or to change casting direction. False casting the same length of line as in the final delivery cast can disturb wary fish. Shooting line on the final delivery cast can often mean the difference between catching fish and just another enjoyable day on the water.

The differences between the classical fly-cast

described in the preceding section and the shooting cast are relatively few. First, the angler's line hand holds the line throughout the cast, until the actual line shoot takes place. After the initial pull to break the water's surface tension, the angler's line hand remains approximately at waist height during the back cast. This acts to lengthen the line between the rod tip and the line hand, thereby shortening the length of line to be straightened on the back cast. Thus, for the same amount of angler energy expended, a higher line velocity is achieved. During the angler's forward cast, his line hand is either lowered or moved to the side away from the rod, in order to keep the line between the line hand and the rod tip the same length. If this length becomes shortened during the forward stroke, additional line slips rearward out beyond the rod tip, reducing the maximum achievable line speed.

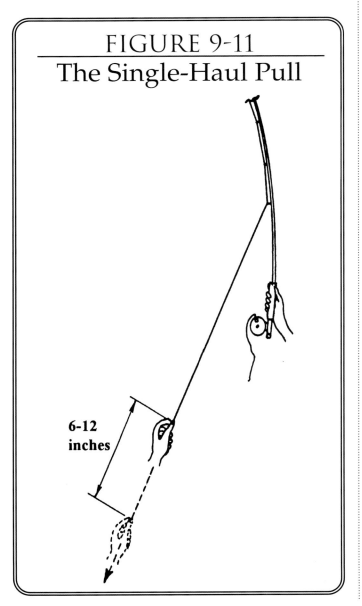

FIGURE 9-11
The Single-Haul Pull

6-12 inches

The final difference from the classical fly-cast is of course the release of the line by the line hand to shoot the line. The timing of this release is critical; if too early or too late, some of the casting energy is wasted. The optimum time for line release is shown on Figure 9-9, position 2, when the rod has straightened and after the angler has suddenly stopped the forward stroke. With about 30 feet of line initially extended beyond the rod tip and with proper casting mechanics, the angler should be able to shoot 10-20 feet of additional line toward the target. The actual amount of line shoot obtained is a function of line speed. The higher line speed developed during the casting stroke, the greater the line's kinetic energy and momentum available to move the line an additional distance. For distance accuracy, it is most important that the fly-fisher be well attuned to his or her shooting capability, so that the target can be consistently hit either at the extreme of the line shoot or by shortening the shoot via line hand friction.

The Single- and Double-Haul

Anglers who fish "big" water (large streams, lakes, estuaries, surf, etc.) inevitably find themselves in situations where another 5-10 feet of cast length is needed to reach the fish. Often, the extended-arm cast, especially in conjunction with a line shoot, will suffice to get the extra needed distance. Additional distance can also be achieved by using either the single-haul or the double-haul technique. Actually, we have already initiated the discussion of hauling techniques through explaining the positioning of the line hand. Referring to Figure 9-11, at this point in the back cast the line hand is normally at near waist height, where it was at the start of the back cast. If, at this point near maximum rod flex, the line hand pulls the line down sharply about 6-12 inches and then immediately returns to its original, waist-high position, the line will be back cast to the rear at a higher speed. This is the single-haul. By developing a higher rearward line speed, the rod is flexed to a greater extent as the extended line slows to a stop. Accordingly, when the angler starts his forward stroke, the rod starts out stiffer and the tip lags behind the rod butt motion to a lesser extent. In other words, the rod tip speeds up sooner, permitting the achievement of higher final line speeds.

The double-haul combines the single-haul with another line pull (haul) at the end of the forward delivery casting stroke. You will remember that experienced fly-casters move their line hand away from the rod hand during the forward casting stroke, in order to prevent the introduction of slack line. By extending this line hand motion even more and sharply, not only does the angler prevent line slack, he also creates additional line speed to contribute to casting distance. It must be emphasized that the preceding descriptions of the single- and double-hauls are just typical of the many variations of this technique that will produce useful results. Hauls of only a few inches are commonly used in small-stream trouting conditions, especially when higher line speeds are needed for accuracy during cross-winds. Though barely perceptible, these subtle hauls can be quite useful if the timing is correct.

In saltwater fishing situations, two-foot hauls can be effective in achieving very high line speeds. The hauls described earlier are two separate actions, each effectively improving its own portion of the overall casting stroke. In one particular version of the double-haul, the angler's first haul is immediately followed by drifting the line hand up and adjacent to the rod hand as the line straightens out at the end of the back cast. Then, both hands move forward together during the forward casting stroke, the line hand suddenly moving away and down during the sudden, hard stop of the rod hand. Although both of these hauls affect different segments of the casting stroke, they appear as one continuous though complex motion. Learning hauling techniques are not recommended until the caster has gained proficiency in basic casting, because of the need for precise timing to achieve longer casts. Similarly, hauling strokes should not be used with fly rods of marginal structural integrity; The single- and double-hauls flex the rod more than in conventional casts, subjecting the rod to fairly high stresses.

Casting Dynamics

A frequent scene in a fly shop is that of a customer wiggling a rod back and forth, to determine its "action" or "feel." Although some people may feel that this is about as useful as kicking the tires on a prospective used car, I always perform this ritual when I pick up a fly rod for the first time. Once I have checked out the fly rod's exterior appearance

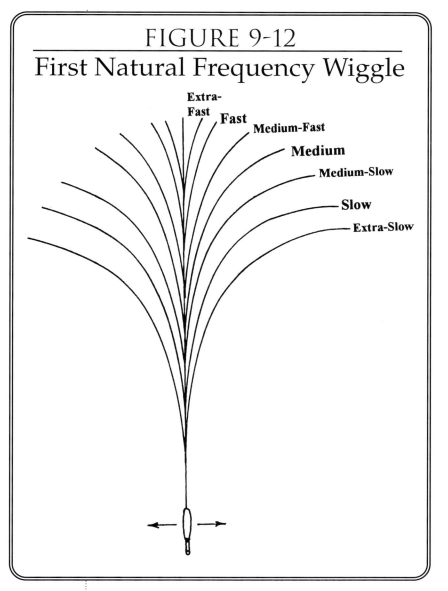

FIGURE 9-12
First Natural Frequency Wiggle

Extra-Fast
Fast
Medium-Fast
Medium
Medium-Slow
Slow
Extra-Slow

and its static bending characteristics, the wiggle test will tell me a lot about its weight balance and whether its action is fast, medium, slow or somewhere in between. For experienced fly-fishers planning a rod purchase, the wiggle test will quickly sort out rods that are not suitable for their purpose and they can spend most of their time test casting the most promising alternatives. On the other hand, the beginner without a significant frame of reference is primarily going through the motions without an objective in mind. The action of a fly rod can be very complex when viewed from a technical perspective, but rather straightforward once one brushes away all of the secondary details. The fly-fishing community generally accepts the terms fast, medium, slow, medium-slow etc. for describing the action of a fly rod.

Figure 9-12 generally depicts the shape of the rod bend during the wiggle test, for the major three classifications of rod action and the four variations thereof. When performing the wiggle test, both hands should grasp the grip firmly with the rod butt pressed against the stomach. A slow, side-to-side, back-and-forth motion should then be established, until the rod oscillates smoothly with only the slightest force required by the angler to maintain this oscillation. When this smooth, repetitive oscillation is established, comparison of the rod bending shape with Figure 9-12 determines its action. In engineering terms, this wiggle test results in the fly rod vibrating at its first natural frequency, a very stable form of oscillation requiring very little angler force to keep it going. A significant

feature of a fly rod's natural frequency is that all parts of the fly rod are moving in concert with one another, resulting in a smooth bending curve with no irregularities.

Routinely, I used to determine the first natural frequency of all the fly rods which I developed or evaluated. The procedure is simple enough to produce consistent readings of natural frequency (cycles per second, where a cycle is defined as the interval between when the rod is fully bent in one direction and when it returns again fully bent in the same direction). My tests on fly rods made from cane, fiberglass, graphite and boron indicated first natural frequencies ranging from 2.0 to 3.0 cycles per second.

Several years ago, Graig Spolek of Portland State University conducted experiments to determine the first natural frequencies of fly rods of many different materials manufactured over a period of many years. This work was first reported to the fly-fishing community in Reference 44, Table A-5. Using a scotch-yoke mechanism per Figure 9-13, Spolek measured fly rod first natural frequencies for rods made of lancewood, greenheart, cane, fiberglass and graphite ranging from 1.18 to 2.62 cycles per second. Not surprisingly, the higher natural frequencies were generally associated with the then-newer, lighter fly rods of the 1970s. The first natural frequency of today's modern graphite fly rods are even higher, especially when adjusted for differences in rod length.

All of the above tests reflect the first natural frequency of the fly rod alone, without reel or line, which provides an accurate quantitative measure of their relative "action." If a standardized test could be agreed upon between fly-rod manufacturers, such measurements would be very useful to the fly-fishing public. These frequency measurements, although useful to compare fly rods, are however not at all indicative of the frequencies of real-life casting situations. Fly-casting is indeed a vibrating system, not unlike the pendulum in a grandfather clock. The pendulum shaft is equivalent to the fly rod except that it doesn't bend. The pendulum weight

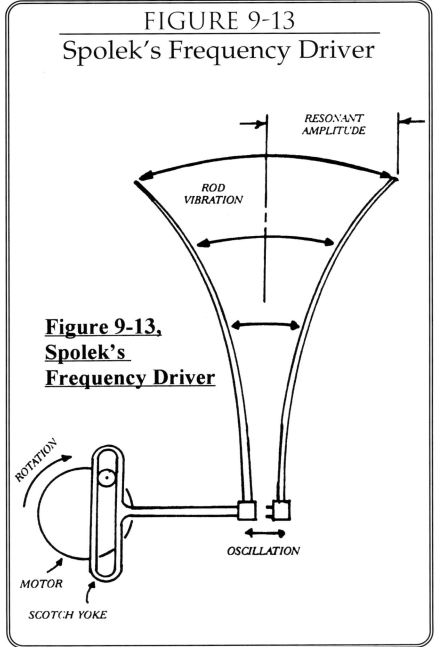

FIGURE 9-13
Spolek's Frequency Driver

RESONANT AMPLITUDE

ROD VIBRATION

Figure 9-13, Spolek's Frequency Driver

ROTATION

OSCILLATION

MOTOR

SCOTCH YOKE

is equivalent to the fly line except that the pendulum weight doesn't change. The clock driver (whether electrical or spring) is equivalent to the angler's force input except that the clock driver input is regular and unchanging. In spite of the complexity of the real-life casting scenario, it too has a first natural frequency, although it is the cumulative integral of the hundreds of instantaneous first natural frequencies produced by the angler as he changes his force signature on the rod during the casting cycle. Stated another way, if the angler's force signature is not smooth and coordinated, the instantaneous frequencies will depart from the inherent first natural frequencies, resulting in uneven rod bending shapes, rod tip wobbling and poor casting results. This does not mean that each combination of fly-rod design, fly line weight and line length extended beyond the rod tip requires a specific casting frequency (cycles or strokes per second). With a given rod, line and line extension length, experienced fly-casters can vary the frequency rate of their casting stroke over a wide range without introducing casting problems. They do this by varying line speed, loop size and rod-tip travel distance.

While Figure 9-12 depicts the rod bending shape when the fly rod is wiggled at its first natural frequency, Figure 9-14 shows the typical bending shape when a fly rod is wiggled at its *second* natural frequency, a much higher frequency rate. This wiggle test is most easily performed by using one hand, because of the higher frequency rate, and by loosening the hand's grip on the rod. If one attempts to wiggle a fly rod at a frequency rate between the first and second natural frequencies, the rod does not flex smoothly; it always wants to vibrate at one of its natural vibrating frequencies. There are also third, fourth and higher natural frequencies, but these vibration rates are generally well beyond the range of practical casting situations. Note that there is a node shown in Figure 9-14 at about three-fourths of the rod's length, where the rod only rotates and doesn't translate back and forth. Some writers have implied some rather mystical qualities to this node, when in fact it is just a point where the dynamics of the upper and lower rod sections are balanced. Every fly rod has a second natural frequency with a node point, though the location of the node point can vary considerably. Higher natural frequencies also have multiple node points.

The importance of the fly rod's second natural frequency is significant, though not necessarily obvious. From Figure 9-14, note that when the rod

butt is being rotated to the left, the rod tip actually moves (or rotates beyond the node) to the right. This phenomenon is seen all too often when fly-casters attempt to initiate the forward casting stroke at too fast a rate. In an actual cast, this early rearward motion creates line slack followed by rod tip droop and undesirable line wobbling. It can also precipitate tailing loops during the forward cast. I often demonstrate this phenomenon during fly-casting presentations by initiating a fly-rod casting stroke with somebody holding a piece of paper about a foot to the rear of the stroke direction. With an initially-slow, controlled casting stroke, the rod tip moves in the correct direction at an increasing speed. If, however, I start the forward stroke with a rapid pulse, the rod tip initially recoils backward, striking the paper loud enough

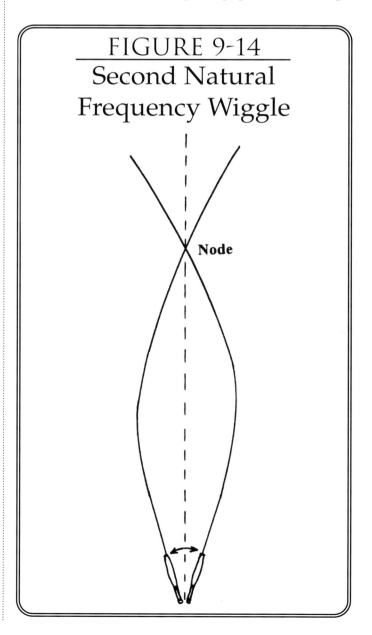

FIGURE 9-14
Second Natural
Frequency Wiggle

Node

to be heard by anyone in the room. This is a classic example of the angler's instantaneous casting stroke frequency rate being much too high for the circumstances. My own tests of cane, fiberglass, graphite and boron fly rods has shown second natural frequencies varying between 4.8 and 6.8 cycles per second, from two to two-and-one-half times the first natural frequency.

As described above, the undesirable introduction of the fly rod's second natural frequency usually occurs at the outset of the forward delivery stroke, because of excessive initial acceleration of the rod. This problem however can also occur at the very end of the forward delivery stroke, when the angler suddenly stops the forward motion of his rod hand. In this case, the rod's deceleration is rather abrupt and the line is beginning to become uncoupled from the rod tip, increasing the rod's second natural frequency. Sequenced strobe photos by Ed Mosser, Figure 9-15, clearly show the beginning of a second natural frequency rod bending shape at position number 5, just before the loop begins to form. There is however no evidence that the introduction of this second natural frequency mode during loop formation is problematic. In fact, it has been suggested by Graig Spolek in Reference 21 of Table A-6 that this last-second introduction of the second natural frequency may even provide additional impetus or energy for higher line speeds.

Damping

Any real vibrating system is subject to damping, or decay of vibration amplitude, in the absence of any external applied forces. Note that the correct term is damping, not dampening. Dampening occurs when you drop your fly rod into the water. Without damping, vibrating systems would continue to vibrate indefinitely, without any decay in amplitude. Damping has always been of interest to fly-fishers, since it

mitigates undesirable rod tip oscillations at the termination of the rearward and forward casting strokes. The causes of damping are many, but they tend to group themselves into four principal areas; aerodynamic, external friction, internal material friction and external applied forces. For fly-casting, these four damping sources are, respectively, air drag on the rod tip and line, friction of the line in the guides and in the ferrules, internal friction between the fibers and the resin, and compensating forces exerted by the angler's hand.

Damping became a popular topic during the 1950s because of the excessive after-bounce of fiberglass fly rods when subjected to high casting stresses. It remains a popular subject to this day, even though most modern fly rods do not have problems with rod tip after-bounce. Unfortunately, for all these years internal material damping has been erroneously identified as the cause or cure for after-bounce. In reality, after-bounce has been caused by a combination of relatively flexible rod tips and relatively heavy rod materials. When fiberglass rods became available, rod designers found they could make rods with

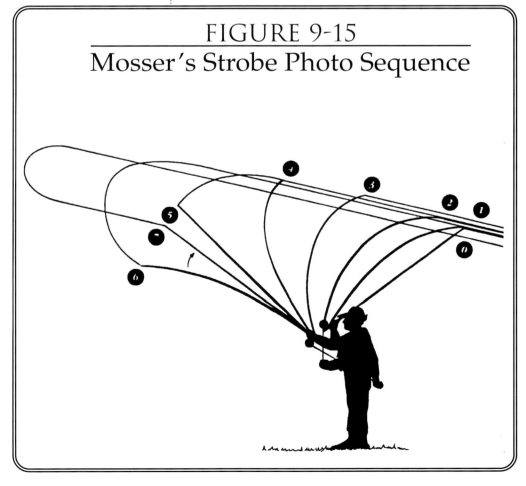

FIGURE 9-15
Mosser's Strobe Photo Sequence

very flexible and strong rod tips. Although these rods were delightful for short to medium casting distances, tip after-bounce became a real problem with long casts. The inertia of the relatively heavy fiberglass material flexed the rod tip excessively and its slowness to recover was ill-timed to the performance of the casting stroke. Then, even after recovery, the rod tip would continue beyond its un-flexed position to flex excessively in the opposite direction. This has absolutely nothing to do with internal material frictional damping. The early fiberglass fly rods were simply designed to favor the short-distance fly-fisher, to the detriment of long-distance casting. Today's modern fiberglass fly rods, especially those made from S-Glass, are much better designed to accommodate the full spectrum of casting needs.

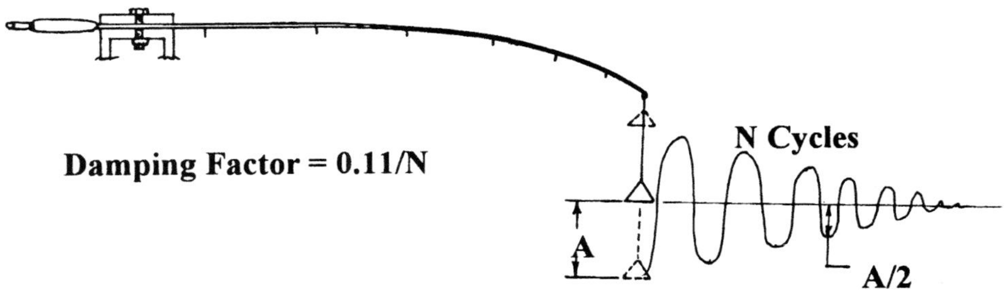

In order to validate my contention that material internal friction isn't important to fly-rod design, let me provide an overview on some of my experiments. Damping is a very important subject in aerospace hardware, especially for propeller and turbine blades. Material damping characteristics are usually determined by a simple test depicted in Figure 9-16. The basics are the same whether the part is a fly rod or a propeller blade. A weight is hung from the rod tip and initially deflected downward a distance A. The weight is then released and the number of oscillations or cycles (N) are counted, until the oscillation amplitude decays to one-half of its original deflection (A/2). Dividing 0.11 by the number of cycles N calculates the damping factor for the rod, a measure of the extent of damping present in the vibrating system. If the damping factor is 1.0, the system is considered fully damped; i.e. the deflected weight simply returns to its original position after release, with no oscillation. By using high rod clamping forces and a weight in the half-ounce range, external friction and aero-dynamic damping forces are minimized and the test produces a good relative measure of internal material damping.

My damping tests of dozens of fly rods have shown that internal material damping is not very

FIGURE 9-16
Damping Factor Test Rig

Damping Factor = 0.11/N

N Cycles

A

A/2

significant. Rods made of synthetic materials such as boron, graphite and fiberglass had damping factors of 0.020 to 0.031, while cane rods had damping factors of from 0.023 to 0.061. Although the difference in damping factors between cane and synthetic rods is indeed significant, all rod materials can be considered to have very low internal material friction or damping; only 2 to 6 percent of fully damped systems. The quick flex recovery of modern graphite rods is due to their tips' combination of high stiffness and light weight, and their minimum after-bounce is due to their low inertia (light weight). I would hasten to add that although internal material damping is relatively unimportant, aerodynamic drag damping is important during casting, because of the relatively high velocities achieved by the rod tip. Also, the angler's grip on the cork handle can be a very important source for rod damping. Just as a very firm grip is important to the sudden stop at the end of the forward delivery cast, a very loose grip immediately afterwards can be most helpful in minimizing rod tip after-bounce.

The State-of-the-Art in Fly-Casting
An overall review of fly-rod technology readily shows that the materials and structural aspects of fly rods are relatively mature and backed up by a broad base of knowledge and design know-how. Such is not the case however with casting and the vibrational and dynamics behavior thereof. We have just literally scratched the surface over the past ten years and there's lots more to learn. The following paragraphs will outline some of the technical activity which is ongoing, and some of the questions that remain to be answered.

For decades there has been a significant debate

in fly-fishing circles as to whether the fly rod acts as a flexible lever or a spring during casting. There is no question that the angler provides all of the energy required to cast the line, leader and fly. The issue is whether or not a significant amount of the angler's energy is stored in the flexed rod and then subsequently imparted to the line as the rod un-flexes or recoils. Many prominent anglers have expounded on the validity of the spring theory; perhaps an equal number have favored the flexible lever. I have always been in the latter camp, because of my basic gut feelings about the casting process and because of the influence of people like Peter Schwab and Vince Marinaro who have been quite adamant about the applicability of the lever theory. To me, it would seem to be impossible to store enough energy in a flexed fly rod, no matter how deeply flexed, to propel line, leader and fly 50-100 feet or more. To confirm this, I tested an older fiberglass fly rod at all different angles and degrees of flex. I was unable to even straighten out 30 feet of line.

More recently, I asked Bill Cairns of the Orvis Company if he would do a casting experiment for me, recording the results of the experiment on the high-speed video recorder that they use in their fly-casting schools. The experiment consisted simply of marking a light-colored fly line with black magic marker at the 30-foot mark and casting with this mark located at the rod tip. The routine was to false cast a few times and then to shoot the line, paying particular photographic attention to the instant when the black mark began to move away from the rod (indicating the beginning of the shoot). If the line shoot began before the rod was un-flexed, that would prove that rod recoil could not contribute to casting distance; once the line and rod tip become uncoupled, the rod cannot add any additional momentum to the line. As it turned out, the background for these video shots was a typical woodsy Vermont fall scene, which made it very difficult to see the movement of the black markings, even with slow, frame-by-frame viewing. Among the dozen or so sequences, however, there were two which clearly showed that the line doesn't begin to shoot until the rod has fully straightened. This of course might have produced different results with a different caster, but I doubt it. This brief test by no means proves that the energy of spring recoil is dominant or even existent in the casting process. It does suggest however that the energy of spring recoil could be a contributor to the energy of line motion. J.M. Robson, author of Reference 23 of Table A-6, in fact suggests that this spring contribution could be as much as 20% of the total energy imparted to the fly rod. Robson's interesting studies are continuing, and I'm sure that he'll offer

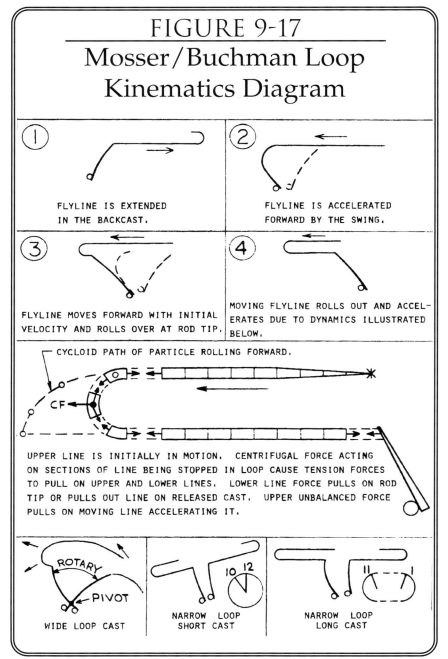

FIGURE 9-17
Mosser/Buchman Loop Kinematics Diagram

① FLYLINE IS EXTENDED IN THE BACKCAST.

② FLYLINE IS ACCELERATED FORWARD BY THE SWING.

③ FLYLINE MOVES FORWARD WITH INITIAL VELOCITY AND ROLLS OVER AT ROD TIP.

④ MOVING FLYLINE ROLLS OUT AND ACCELERATES DUE TO DYNAMICS ILLUSTRATED BELOW.

CYCLOID PATH OF PARTICLE ROLLING FORWARD.

CF

UPPER LINE IS INITIALLY IN MOTION. CENTRIFUGAL FORCE ACTING ON SECTIONS OF LINE BEING STOPPED IN LOOP CAUSE TENSION FORCES TO PULL ON UPPER AND LOWER LINES. LOWER LINE FORCE PULLS ON ROD TIP OR PULLS OUT LINE ON RELEASED CAST. UPPER UNBALANCED FORCE PULLS ON MOVING LINE ACCELERATING IT.

ROTARY
PIVOT
WIDE LOOP CAST

NARROW LOOP SHORT CAST

NARROW LOOP LONG CAST

future technical insight on casting to the fly-fishing community.

In general, much more needs to be learned about the dynamic behavior of a fly rod, particularly at the end of the forward delivery stroke, when so much is going on. Part of the required knowledge must come from the behavior of the line as it is unrolling. Figure 9-17 is a graphic by Ed Mosser from Reference 20 of Table A-5, which illustrates how energy is transferred from the decelerated stationary portion of the line to the still-moving line portion. Although this book is primarily intended to discuss the fly rod and not the fly line, it is quite clear that knowledge of line dynamics is critical to understanding how the line loads the fly rod during casting.

A number of unknowns exist in the search for information which will fully define the fly-cast and all of its parameters. Defining the angler's casting stroke and all of its kinematic and acceleration rate variations is one of the most important areas needing attention. Then, this spectrum of information needs to be integrated with the geometric and dynamic characteristics of flexible fly rods, to determine the velocity/time patterns of straight-line and curved rod tip paths. And, finally, these rod-tip paths must be studied in conjunction with various line lengths and designs to determine the resultant cast patterns and features. Does all of this knowledge make one a better fly-fisherman? I doubt it, but it should produce information to permit improved casting strokes, rod designs and line designs.

A few decades ago, the golfing industry was where we are today in the fly-fishing industry. Good golf swings were being practiced but were not fully defined. Club heads and shafts were quite advanced, but nowhere to the extent that they are today. Golf balls have also been significantly improved over the years. Technology has played an important role in improving golf equipment, in spite of all the excessive marketing hyperbole which always accompanies new products. An important part of golf's technology growth can be attributed to the development of the "Iron Byron," that club-swinging robot that can be programmed to reproduce specific golf swings, time after time. With the Iron Byron, club makers and ball manufacturers have been able to objectively evaluate alternative product designs. Just as important, the various generic types of club heads and shafts have been classified with respect to their flex level, kick point, torsional stiffness, etc., giving the golfer more identifiable choices in product selection and giving the equipment manufacturers a broader product spectrum.

I believe that the fly-fishing industry could be well served by the development of a programmable casting robot, designed to reproduce the casting motions of a broad range of fly-fishers. To the best of my knowledge, there is no current effort planned in this direction. Perhaps that will change in the future, if the number of fly-fishers grows to a market size which can adequately support such an expenditure. This type of development effort is not inexpensive, and the required equipment and instrumentation would be rather sophisticated. Of course, there are certainly organizations thinking toward this direction and the quality of the technical references listed in Table A-6 suggests that some of the analytical groundwork is being made. Frank Paul and Paul Joseph of Clemson University have some interesting concepts along these lines and one of their Masters degree students, Robert Haun has published his thesis on the dynamic modeling of multi-sectioned fly rods (Reference 26, Table A-6). Haun's work in defining fly-rod natural frequency mode shapes with different ferrule designs is particularly interesting. Other areas which Paul and Joseph hope to pursue are high-speed vision detection systems for measuring the kinematic motions of fly-casters and various aspects of casting robot design. I'm sure that there are many other pockets of useful research across the country, but there seems to be no effort to coordinate their content.

Chapter 10
THE FLY-ROD DESIGN PROCESS

Long before there were any useful techniques for designing fly rods, fly rods were nevertheless made and successfully fished. As conjectured in Chapter 2, the first fly rods were probably just cut from growing saplings, fitted with a tip-top, tied to a line and leader and fished. With experience, these first rod makers probably became quite selective with regard to wood species, diameter/length, number of knots, etc. And eventually, as fly-fishers became more proficient in casting and fish-fighting, rod makers most certainly began to whittle or shave these saplings so that the resultant tapers met the needs of the early fly-fishers with regard to flexibility, stiffness and weight. And surely, when these wooden fly rods began to gain acceptance, the dimensions and specifications for these rods were duly recorded and used to make duplicates and improvements. It is thus likely that the earliest fly rods slowly evolved and improved without any regimented design process other than documented tabulations of dimensions and procedures.

History shows that this evolutionary design approach continued through the development of cane fly rods, with the manufacturing details of thousands of fly rods reflected in the precision settings of beveling machines and planing forms. When cane rod dimensions didn't work out well, the "design" was either scrapped in its entirety or adjusted somewhat and tried again. This so-called "make-'em and break-'em" approach has continued to some extent even today. It is certainly the fastest and least expensive (over the near-term, at least) way to evaluate a proposed new concept. Also, given a sufficient number of successful past designs, the success ratio increases for future designs through extrapolation and interpolation. Nevertheless, the basic problem with exclusive reliance on rod dimensions is that the introduction of new materials having different structural characteristics renders the dimensional information rather useless. Certainly, the cane tapers were of little utility when fiberglass first came on the scene. Likewise, the fiberglass pattern dimensions and mandrel dimensions were of marginal usefulness when graphite came on the scene. Even now, as new fibers and new resins are introduced, the process of extrapolation and interpolation becomes very difficult. Accordingly, it is believed that more fundamental design processes are needed, processes which focus on the universal characteristics of fly rods such as flexural shape, stiffness, strength and dynamic behavior. The purpose of this chapter is to review some of the more sophisticated design processes which have been used and developed over the years.

Static Deflection Profiling

For many years, rod makers and fly-fishers have rigged various means to clamp the fly-rod grip to a wall, hang a weight from the rod tip-top and trace the resultant flexural profile onto the wall or paper backing. With a large number of tracings and considerable fishing experience, the deflection shape, the tip deflection distance and the weight can be correlated with line weight and rod action. Although this technique has little utility in designing fly rods, it can be quite helpful in evaluating and classifying rods and rod prototypes. One of the limitations of this technique is the inability to view the entire rod's flexural shape profile. For example, if a relatively light weight is hung from the tip-top, this provides a good measure of the flexural profile of the tip section but has insufficient weight to deflect the butt section to any measurable degree. Conversely, if a very heavy weight is hung from the tip-top which does in fact deflect the rod's butt section, the rod's tip section is essentially straightened out and there is no tip flexural shape to evaluate. This technique also fails to recognize the dynamic character of a fly rod; especially its distributed weight, which significantly affects the fly rod's flexural shape due to inertial loading during casting. The aerodynamic characteristics of the fly rod are also ignored during static deflection testing. A final, though relatively minor deficiency in this technique is that almost all practitioners hang the weight from the tip-top, rather from a line strung through the rod's line guides, which more closely duplicates the distributed line loading on the rod.

As reviewed in Reference 44 of Table A-5, Graig Spolek has done considerable research in flexural profiling, using the relatively sophisticated instrumentation setup shown in Figure 10-1. The static deflection technique has been and still is used by many rod manufacturers, though with more simplified instrumentation and recording techniques. Very recently, the Orvis Company began using an interesting static deflection technique, shown pictorially in Figure 10-2. With this test setup, a flex point A is established, a distance B from the butt end and a distance C from the tip end. The distances B and C are then used in a formula to establish a flex index for that fly rod. Orvis now uses these flex indexes to classify all of their fly rods. The test itself is also used for quality control purposes, to ensure consistency within production runs of particular fly-rod models. Orvis has also begun to use a more sophisticated method of measuring the weight of their fly rods, using a fulcrum at the grip and a weight at the reel seat, to measure the overhung weight of the rod blank. This is a more realistic indicator of how heavy the fly rod feels in the angler's hand. Both the flex and overhung weight setups are quite similar to test rigs used in the golf club industry to measure flex level, kick-point and swing weight.

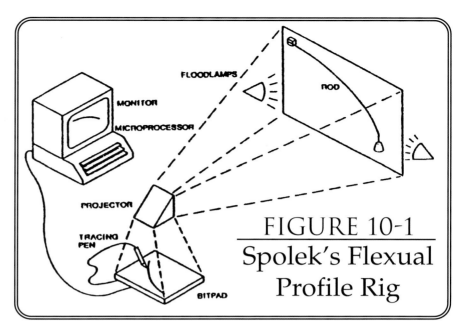

FIGURE 10-1
Spolek's Flexual Profile Rig

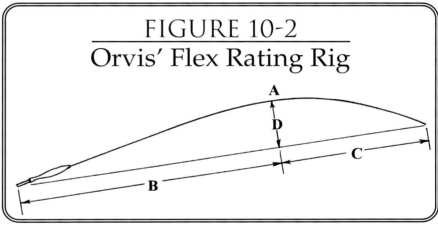

FIGURE 10-2
Orvis' Flex Rating Rig

Stress Profiling

Most of the early cane rod makers were quite secretive about the techniques that they used to make their cane rods and the basis for their dimensional tapers. Everett Garrison (1893-1975) may have been at one time equally silent about his rod design techniques, but in his twilight years he unselfishly shared his decades of experience with the fly-fishing world. Hoagy B. Carmichael, television producer and son of the famous songwriter and composer Hoagy Carmichael, worked with Garrison over a period of many months to photograph his rod-making equipment and to document his approaches to cane fly-rod design. The results of this effort were captured in a 1977 book authored by Garrison and Carmichael, Reference 8, Table A-4. This book has been well-received by the cane-rod-making community and has been a standard reference for many beginning cane practitioners.

In the mid-1970s I had the privilege to meet Garrison's widow, Charlotte, and to review his rod-making equipment. Hoagy Carmichael had asked me to come to New York state for this purpose, but also to review Garrison's notes for their consistency. As a civil engineer, Garrison was well-versed in structures and mechanics and this background was evident in his technical notes. I found all of Garrison's notes to be consistent with accepted mechanical engineering (my field) practice, with only two remaining questions. An essential ingredient in Garrison's design process is a stress curve, a plot of cane rod stress at various stations along the length of the fly rod. Figure 10-3 is a reproduction of one of Garrison's many stress curves, documenting the desired stress levels in a typical, good fly-rod design. Garrison's writings indicated that he had performed many stress tests of cane-rod sections which undoubtedly formed the basis for these curves. However, I was never able to determine how these curves were derived; i.e. how the stress values were calculated. The other remaining question relates to the use of an impact factor to multiply the static moments calculated from the process, reflecting the dynamics of the casting process. The need for such a factor is evident, since the static moment calculations reflect the weight elements of the fly rod, but not the inertial constituents brought into play during the reversals of the casting stroke. I could not, however, find any basis for determining the impact factor for any given rod design. Although the basis for the stress curves and impact factor may never be known, there is no doubt that the cane rod designs by Garrison resulted in excellent casting tools that are held in high regard by the fly-fishing community.

It would be outside the scope of this book to document Garrison's design procedures, especially since Reference 8 of Table A-4 covers this in considerable detail. In essence though, the static moments of all of the rod's components (blank sections, guides, windings, varnish, etc) are calculated and factored for impact. Then, the bending stresses are calculated for every 5-inch interval along the rod's length and compared to the stress curve. Since the first try inevitably produces variances between the design objective stress values and the calculated stresses, the rod blank diametral dimensions are adjusted and the process repeated until the calculated and design objective stresses are the same. It will usually take only two or three such iterations to achieve stress agreement.

Stiffness Profiling

When I was first faced with the challenge of designing and making fly rods from a brand new material, boron, I was undoubtedly in the same position as the early fiberglass rod makers. Without a prior design data base to rely on, this was a formidable challenge. The earliest graphite fly rod manufacturers also had a similar dilemma, though they at least had the fiberglass technology design base as a starting point. Since boron was a fibrous material quite unlike fiberglass (or graphite), I literally had

to start at the ground floor. After due consideration of many alternatives, I decided that the best design baseline was to analyze the stiffness characteristics of current fly rods which were generally accepted in the industry. I elected not to use the overall static deflection curves described earlier in this chapter, because of their deficiencies and their inability to produce useful engineering data. Standard cantilever beam equations were what I needed to use, but those equations are not valid for highly tapered structures nor for structures undergoing very high deflection.

Eventually, I decided to subject existing fly rods to a standard cantilever beam test, evaluating each

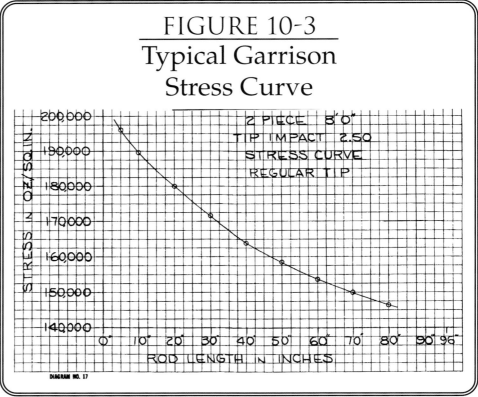

rod only six inches at a time. Figure 10-4 depicts the test rig which I constructed and successfully used for nearly 15 years. This technique was first disclosed to the fly-fishing community via Reference 1 of Table A-5, in 1973. The standard equation for determining stiffness of a cantilever beam is:

$EI = Pl^3/3y$, where; EI = rod section stiffness
in pound-inches squared
P = applied load in pounds
l = length of test section
in inches
y = deflection under load
in inches

This equation is accurate only for relatively small deflections, which makes it ideal for testing short sections of a fly rod. Also, since the equation assumes a constant EI or stiffness throughout the test section, the test actually measures the average EI within the six-inch test section.

Accordingly, I consistently assumed that this EI was the EI at the midpoint of the test section, which was a reasonable approximation for my purposes. I was thus able to draw design objective stiffness profile curves per Figures 6-5 and 6-6. These would thus become the standards or objectives to aim for in developing my line of boron fly rods.

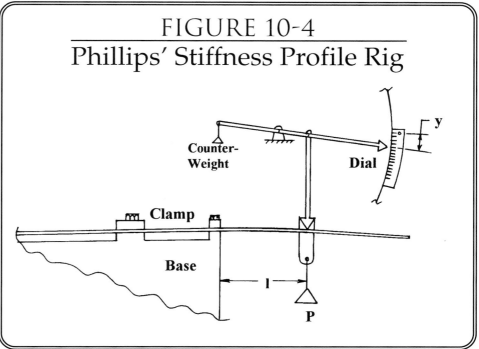

FIGURE 10-4
Phillips' Stiffness Profile Rig

Through microphotographs of cured boron/epoxy test sections I was able to confirm that my fabrication process was producing fiber volume fractions of around 50%, typical of most industry-quality manufacturing. Accordingly, the modulus of elasticity, E, of these boron rod sections was approximately 56 million psi x 0.50 or 28 million psi. If therefore I needed an EI of 500 pound-inches squared at a particular point in the rod, I would be able to achieve that stiffness level by making sure that the Moment of Inertia I of that cross-section was 500/28 million, or 0.0000178 inches[4], or a diameter of 0.138 inches.(I = $\pi d^4/64$). This diameter corresponds to a cross-sectional area of 0.0150 square inches. Since the cross-sectional area of each boron fiber is 0.0000245 square inches, this means that approximately 306 fibers are needed at that point in the fly rod (0.0150x0.50/.0000245). With standard 5.6 mil boron/epoxy prepreg tape containing 200 fibers per inch width of tape, this requires the tape pattern at that point to be 306/200 or 1.5 inches wide. In practice, this calculation procedure became quite tedious and I found that I was able to determine local tape pattern width directly from stiffness by using a single generic design curve.

Prototype boron fly rods were then tested in the rig of Figure 10-4, and they usually agreed quite closely with the design objective curve. When the blanks were then fitted with guides, grip, reel seat, etc. and then test cast, they performed astonishingly well and always outdistanced their cane or fiberglass predecessor. Unfortunately, I also found that they were not particularly well suited to the sometimes delicate casting and fishing conditions required in my home streams of the Farmington River in Connecticut, the Beaverkill River in New York and especially the Battenkill River in Vermont and New York. What was happening was that the stiffness levels were quite closely matched throughout the length of the rod, but the extremely light-weight and small-diameter tip sections were not bending enough to easily obtain straight-line rod tip travel during casting. Both the low inertia and the low aerodynamic profile were contributing to this lack of tip section bending. My solution was to make some significant design changes to reduce tip diameters down to as low as 0.040 inches. This lowered the EI levels in the tip considerably, achieving the required flexural profiles and at the same time improving line speeds by decreasing aerodynamic and inertial losses. And so, stiffness profiling was an excellent way to match the stiffness characteristics of proven fly-rod designs, but further refinement was needed to produce an all-around, good fly-fishing instrument.

Fly-Rod Design by Computer

The modern digital computer has revolutionized industrial processes over the past two decades, leading in most cases to improved products and processes at markedly reduced costs. Nowhere has this revolution been more pronounced and welcomed than in the aerospace industry, where I spent my working career. Seemingly endless streams of complex calculations and mathematical models have been reduced to time intervals approaching the blink of an eye, often under the real-time control of the designer or manufacturing engineer. The digital computer has of course also leaped into the fly-rod industry, assisting such functions as order processing, market analysis, production control, financial accounting, design data bases, etc.

From the design and manufacturing viewpoint, however, the best is certainly yet to come. Let me list just a few of the innovations that could be on the horizon if the fly-rod market grows enough to justify the required investments:

- Standard classification systems for fly-rod designs
- Quantitative casting performance criteria linked to specific fly-fishing scenarios
- Mathematical models of various types of casting strokes, capable of producing casting simulations with specific fly-rod designs
- Real-time simulation of fly-casting, showing how changes in rod design affect the geometry of the cast
- Mathematical models of the fly-rod flexural shape during casting, with the location of maximum stresses identified and quantified
- Automated high-speed cutting of prepreg tape patterns, sequenced for minimum scrap and "just-in-time" scheduling
- Automated quality assurance testing of completed blanks and rods
- Rod design optimization programs capable of minimizing rod weight with various combinations of fiber orientation and properties

Computers of course will play important roles in developing these types of innovations and especially in the integration of these systems with one another. Will any of this happen? Frankly, I don't know. It depends on the future size of the market, the degree of cooperation within the fly-fishing community, the industry's perception of the importance of this level of technology involvement, and a host of other factors. What I am sure of is that these innovations are feasible, thanks to the existence and future growth of the modern digital computer.

EPILOGUE

In the preceding chapters I've reviewed how technology has impacted fly rods over the years, from the contributions of individual craftsmen to the major advances spawned by the aerospace industry. As a result, today's modern fly rods offer the following advantages over the rods of the past:

- Today's rods are much lighter and therefore less tiring and capable of being cast for longer periods of time
- Casting distance has been considerably extended over the years, due to higher attainable line speeds
- In many instances, the higher line speeds have permitted more accurate presentations (crosswinds)
- The 3- to 7-piece rods are much more travel-friendly, giving the fly-fisher more fishing options
- A wider range of actions and lengths are available to suit essentially any individual's needs
- The new, synthetic materials are essentially impervious to moisture and resistant to wear under normal use
- Relatively speaking, good fly rods are now available at lower prices

Because of the above, fly-fishing is accessible to many more people than ever, even those with modest incomes, marginal casting skills and not enough patience to learn the many subtle intricacies of fly-fishing. This has the potential for greater political clout when fighting environmental, conservation and fisheries management issues. It must be obvious to the reader that the author is high on technology; perhaps even a bit of a fanatic at times. That's a natural result of my work background, I suppose. However, I'm keenly aware of the fact that fly-fishing doesn't really need technology to provide enjoyment and sport to its participants. Surely, nineteenth-century fly-fishers didn't enjoy their sport any less than we do today. Enjoyment of our sport is more based upon the availability and challenge of our prey, plus the beauty, health and solitude of our fishing surroundings. And so, as famous radio journalist Paul Harvey says, it's now time "for the rest of the story."

Technology is a two-edged sword. While its benefits attract more fly-fishers, at some point the numbers could overwhelm our fishing waters. Rationed use of public waters and increased fee-based private waters may make our fishing waters look more like crowded ski resorts and golf courses. Perhaps this will be self-regulating, culling out the would-be angler who is intent on instant gratification or higher catch/cost ratios. If technology creates a cadre of higher-skilled fly-fishers, this also places higher pressure on our fish resources. This and greater numbers of anglers could promulgate a tendency to fall back to the old put-and-take philosophy of public hatcheries. Accordingly, the genes of the wild fish that we seek to catch could be diluted by the intrusion of their inferior cousins.

Technology has the potential for mitigating the pollution that threatens the health of our fishing waters. And yet, the profit motive more commonly drives the use of technology to build new roads, shopping centers, homes, and high-rises. Such uses invariably hurt rather than help our fisheries and fishing waters, through concentration of runoff, increasing population density, lowered water tables, etc. This is of course not the fault of technology, but rather the fault of governments and, inevitably its citizens (us) for permitting the extent of such development. Whereas technology has clearly helped to improve fly rods, it remains to be seen whether it will help to improve fly-fishing. It's up to you and me to influence the eventual outcome.

Tight Lines!
Don Phillips
4/15/99

GLOSSARY OF TECHNICAL TERMS

The following glossary of terms will help some readers in understanding the technical terms used in this book. Wherever appropriate, the most relevant Webster's Dictionary definitions will be used, or the author's definitions which are unique to the technology of fly rods.

Acceleration: Increase in velocity or speed. Usually measured in units of ft/sec^2.

Action, fly rod: The behavior of a fly rod during the process of casting.

Abduction, wrist: Extension of the wrist rearward, in the plane of the hand.

Adduction, wrist: Extension of the wrist forward, in the plane of the hand.

Amorphous: Having no apparent crystalline form and exhibiting comparable properties in all directions.

Anisotropic: Exhibiting properties with different values when measured in different directions.

Area: The surface included within a set of lines. Usually measured in units of square inches or square feet.

Axis: A line around which a body or figure is symmetrical.

Balsa Wood: Wood from the balsa, a tropical American tree.

Bending Plane: The plane formed by the axis of a bent rod.

Beveling Machine: A machine tool for milling cane rod strips into splines.

Blank, green: A fishing rod blank before being cured into a cohesive structural unit.

Blank, rod: A fishing rod before being assembled with line guides, grip, reel seat, etc.

Bonding: Being held together with a chemical or a mechanical bond.

Borax: Hydrated sodium borate, the source for boron in boron fibers.

Bounce, tip: Undesirable rod tip motion during a casting stroke.

Brittle: Tending to crack or break with relatively little deformation.

Buckling, fiber: Lateral fiber displacement when subjected to a longitudinal compressive force.

Cane Fly Rods, Calcutta: Fly rods made from an Indian bamboo, *Gigantochloa macrostachya*.

Cane Fly Rods, double-built: Fly rods incorporating two layers of cane splines, one outside the other.

Cane Fly Rods, fluted: Fly rods whose cane splines have been hollowed, still maintaining significant glue bond area between splines.

Cane Fly Rods, scalloped: Fly rods whose cane splines have been hollowed, at various segments along the rod.

Cane Fly Rods, spiraling-strip: Fly rods whose cane splines have been glued and cured in the twisted position.

Cane Fly Rods, Tonkin: Fly rods made from tea-stick bamboo, from the Kwangtung province of China.

Cane Nodes: Enlarged, annular surface discontinuities along the length of a cane culm.

Cantilever Beam: A projecting beam supported at only one end.

Cast: Throwing a line, leader and fly with a fishing rod.

Cast, back: A cast in the rearward direction, opposite to the direction of the forward delivery cast.

Cast, classical fly: A casting sequence consisting of line pickup, back cast and a forward delivery cast.

Cast, double-haul: Technique for increasing line speed during both the back cast and the forward delivery cast.

Cast, extended-arm: Technique for increasing line speed during the forward delivery cast.

Cast, forward delivery: The final forward cast, delivering the fly to the target.

Cast, single-haul: Technique for increasing line speed during the backcast.

Casting Dynamics: The mechanics of fly-casting, especially the forces and motions of the fly rod, line, leader and fly.

Casting, false: Repeated back casts and forward casts, without delivering the fly on the water.

Casting Frequency: The rate of casting stroke cycles per minute or per second.

Casting Plane: The plane formed by the flexed rod, line and line loop, when all are in the same plane.

Casting Simulation: Electronic/mathematical

modeling of the angler, rod, line, leader and fly during casting.

Casting Stroke: The motions of the angler's body parts during casting.

Centerline, rod: The axis of the fly rod, throughout its length.

Chemical Properties: The chemical behavior of materials relative to bonding, reaction to other materials, etc.

Cloth Patterns: The shape of the prepreg being wrapped on the mandrel.

Coatings, polymer: Chemical compounds used to coat rods, thread wraps, etc.

Coatings, preservative: Coatings used to maintain the original color of thread wrappings.

Coatings, silane: Silicon-based coatings to maintain moisture-resistant bonding between fiberglass fibers and resins.

Coatings, sizing: Fiber coatings designed to improve bonding between fibers and resins.

Compaction: Squeezing the green blank with shrink tape or tubing, to eliminate gaseous voids and excess resin.

Composite Materials: Material systems composed of high-performance elements imbedded in a softer matrix.

Composite Materials, bidirectional: Composite materials with high-performance fibers or whiskers oriented in two, usually mutually perpendicular, directions.

Composite Materials, unidirectional: Composite materials with high-performance fibers or whiskers, all oriented in one direction.

Concave: Hollowed or rounded inward, like the inside of a bowl.

Conductivity, electrical: The extent of a material's ability to transmit electricity.

Conductivity, thermal: The extent of a material's ability to transmit heat.

Convex: Curved or rounded like the exterior of the surface of a circle or sphere.

Corrosion Resistance: The ability of a material or coating to resist corrosion.

Cross-Section: A view of the cut edge of a rod which has been sliced at right angles to its axis.

Crystalline Structure: Material with a regularly repeating atomic structure, formed by solidification.

Culm: The stem or stalk of bamboo.

Curing Oven: Oven used to heat, cure and harden the resins in green fishing rod blanks.

Damping: The decay of amplitude in a vibrating beam or structure.

Damping, aerodynamic: Damping caused by air friction.

Damping, force: Damping caused by externally-applied forces or moments.

Damping, friction: Damping caused by friction, either internal material friction or externally-applied friction.

Damping Factor: The numerical ratio of damping in a given system to the damping in a fully-damped system.

Dapping: Presenting the fly on the water by dangling it under the fly rod's tip-top.

Deceleration: Decrease in velocity or speed. Usually expressed in units of feet/sec^2.

Deflection: Movement or displacement of a body when subjected to a force or moment.

Deformation: Change in shape or dimensions of a body when subjected to a force or moment.

Deformation, elastic: Deformation which disappears when the force or moment is removed.

Deformation, permanent: Deformation which at least partially remains when force or moment is removed.

Density: Weight per unit of volume, usually expressed in units of lbs/in3 or gms/cc3.

Denier: The unit of fineness for a yarn, where "1" is the fineness of 1 gram of yarn whose length is 9000 meters.

Design Optimization: Design process which adjusts many variables until an optimum design is achieved.

Dodecagon: A 12-sided regular polygon.

Drift, rod: Letting the rod drift to the rear during the back cast, to perform the extended-arm cast.

Dynamic Modeling: Simulation of the line motions and rod vibration characteristics during casting.

Eccentricity: The condition of a hollow rod, when its inner and outer diameters are based upon different center lines.

Effective Rod Length: Perpendicular moment arm distance between the rod grip and the fly line extended beyond the fly rod tip-top.

Elastic Range: Range of loads which permits deformation to be fully reversed upon load removal.

Elastomeric "O" Rings: Rubber rings of circular cross-section used in aluminum ferrules to increase holding friction between the engaged halves.

Electrodeposition: A process used to vapor-deposit elemental boron onto a tungsten wire.

Elongation: The percent lengthening of a rod or fiber when subjected to tensile forces along its axis.

Expansion, thermal: Increase in material dimensions when subjected to increasing temperature.

Extrapolation: Estimating results by extending the trends of existing data.

Ferrule: Short tubes or bushings to join rod sections together.

Ferrule, cushioned: A ferrule employing elastic material between ferrule and rod, to soften the interface between the two.

Ferrule, doweled: A ferrule with a central dowel and mating receptacle, to minimize relative lateral motion.

Ferrule, feralite: A fiberglass ferrule whose female half is integral with the fly rod's tip section.

Ferrule, flared-butt: A nickel-silver ferrule employing a large-diameter female half and single-wall construction.

Ferrule, friction-fit: Ferrule relying upon engagement friction to keep both halves together.

Ferrule, Kosmic: A nickel-silver ferrule employing cushioning and serration for softening.

Ferrule, serrated: A nickel-silver ferrule with serrations at both ends for softening.

Ferrule, shouldered: A nickel-silver ferrule with a reduced-diameter engagement surface.

Ferrule, sleeve: A composite material ferrule employing an outer sleeve to join both rod sections.

Ferrule, spigot: A composite material ferrule employing an internal rod to join both rod sections.

Ferrule, super-z: A nickel-silver ferrule employing double-wall tubing over the lower rod section.

Ferrule, waterproof: A nickel-silver ferrule with a moisture-barrier at the base of the female receptacle.

Ferrule, welted: A nickel-silver ferrule with a reinforcing-ring at the outer end of the female half, to stiffen its circular shape.

Ferrule Engagement Surface: The joining area of the two ferrule halves, whose friction keeps them together.

Fibers, boron: Fibers produced by the electro-deposition of boron on a tungsten wire.

Fibers, collimated: Fibers arranged in one plane, all fibers parallel and equidistant from one another.

Fibers, fiberglass: Fibers produced by spinning hot, molten glass, followed by rapid cooling.

Fibers, graphite: Fibers produced by the pyrolysis of rayon, pitch or polyacrylonitrile (PAN) fibers.

Fibers, Kevlar: A proprietary aramid fiber manufactured by DuPont.

Flex Index: Classification of fly rod flex types into a standard numerical scale.

Flex Level: The amount of fly rod tip deflection when loaded with a static weight.

Flex Point: The rod location which is the greatest perpendicular distance from a line drawn between the grip and the tip-top, while the rod is undergoing static deflection testing.

Force: An external load imposed on a body of material.

Force, axial: A force imposed on a symmetrical body along its axis. Also called a longitudinal force.

Force, compressive: A force tending to squeeze a material together.

Force, distributed: A force distributed over an area of contact. Also called pressure.

Force, lateral: A force whose direction is perpendicular to the axis of a symmetrical body. Also called a radial force.

Force, longitudinal: A force whose direction coincides with the axis of a symmetrical body. Also called an axial force.

Force, radial: A force directed toward or away from the center of a spherical or cylindrical body. Also called a lateral force.

Force, shear: A force tending to slide material past fixed material along a plane of contact.

Force, surface tension: A viscous force at the free surface of water which tends to oppose the lifting of a fly line from the water.

Force, tensile: A force tending to stretch a material apart.

Frequency Mode Shapes: The shape of a rod while vibrating at one of its natural frequencies.

Friction: Resistance to relative motion between two contacting surfaces.

Friction, coefficient of: A measure of the friction force between two surfaces having sliding contact.

Friction, ferrule: The force keeping ferrule halves from separating during fly rod use.

Friction, internal: Forces within composite materials when deformed under stress.

Friction, line guide: Friction forces between a line guide and a moving line.

Fulcrum: The central point of support for a lever system.

Glues, natural: Adhesives from natural materials such as animal hides.

Glues, synthetic: Chemically-synthesized adhesives.

Hardness: The resistance of a material's surface against scratching or penetration by another material.

Helical Wraps: Fiber placement in a fly rod to increase its hoop strength and resistance to crushing.

Heptagon: A 7-sided polygon.

Hexagon: A 6-sided polygon.

Hook Keeper: A ring or other retention device mounted on a fly rod to engage the fly hook when not fishing.

Impact Factor: A numerical factor, usually derived experimentally, which multiplies static forces or moments to reflect the higher values usually experienced under dynamic conditions.

Inertia: A basic property of matter by which it tends to stay at rest or remain at a constant directional velocity, unless acted upon by an external force.

Interpolation: Estimating results by inference, based upon similar existing data.

Just-In-Time Scheduling: The queuing of assembly parts so that they are available when and where required to meet customer delivery requirements.

Kick-Point: The flex point for a golf club shaft.

Kinematics: The study of dynamics, especially the aspects of position and motion.

Kinetic Energy: The energy of a moving body of material, $1/2\ mv^2$, where m is the mass (weight/gravitational constant) and v is the velocity of the body. Usually expressed in units of pound-feet.

Knurled: A ridged or beaded surface on metal, to aid in gripping or turning.

Layup, pattern: Positioning the prepreg tape pattern around the mandrel.

Linear: A process where an output is directly proportional to its input.

Line Belly: That portion of the fly line which has the largest, constant diameter.

Line Guides: Fly rod components that are designed to guide the fly line during the line shoot and to distribute line forces along the rod.

Line Guides, agate: Guides using agate rings to contain the fly line.

Line Guides, braced: Guides whose rings are braced for rigidity.

Line Guides, ceramic: Guides whose rings are made from a ceramic or cermet material.

Line Guides, double foot: Guides attached to the fly rod with two feet.

Line Guides, ring-and-keeper: Older guides using hinged rings to contain the line.

Line Guides, single-foot: Guides attached to the fly rod with one foot.

Line Guides, snake: Guides employing a spiraling wire to contain the line.

Line Guides, stripping: The one or two guides located closest to the rod grip.

Line Guides, tunnel: Older guides using flared hollow cylinders to contain the line.

Line Mending: Throwing upstream line loops while fishing, to prevent fly drag.

Line Pickup: Getting the fly line in the air, to initiate the back cast.

Line Pressure: Lateral forces exerted on the line guides by the fly line.

Line Pull: The tugging force on the line and rod tip, as the line unrolls during casting.

Line Release: The point when the angler lets go of the line during the shoot.

Line Shooting: The end of the forward delivery cast, when line between the rod's tip-top and the reel is drawn out beyond the tip-top.

Line Tension: An axial, tensile force in the fly line.

Lubricity: The characteristic of a material to self-lubricate its surface during contact, to minimize friction and wear.

Mandrel: A long, slender form which provides the foundation for the fly rod's composite material.

Mandrel, permanent: A mandrel which remains with the fly rod during its life.

Mandrel, removable: A mandrel which is removed after oven curing, forming a hollow fly rod.

Mass: The property of a body denoting its inertial potential in a gravitational field. Its weight divided by the gravitational constant of 32.2; usually expressed in units of lbs-sec^2/foot.

Material Properties: The characteristics and behavior of a material.

Mathematical Model: The behavior of a component or system, as expressed in a numerical math model.

Matrix Material: The base material surrounding the fibers in a composite material.

Mechanical Properties: The mechanical behavior of a material subjected to stresses, forces and moments.

Mixtures, rule of: A basic rule of composite materials which states that the mechanical properties of the composite material are proportional to the mechanical properties of the high-performance fibers. This proportionality is dependent upon the volume fraction of the fibers and the extent to which the fibers are oriented in the working direction.

Modulus, bulk: The stiffness or flexibility of rubber, resin, or other relatively soft materials. Usually expressed in units of lbs/in^2.

Modulus of Elasticity: The stiffness or resistance to deformation of high performance materials when stressed in their elastic range, usually expressed in units of lbs/in^2. Also referred to as Young's Modulus.

Moment: A torque or force exerted on a body over a moment arm, so as to cause the body to rotate.

Moment, static: A moment applied to a body, where the body remains stationary during load application.

Natural Frequency: A vibration or oscillation rate which persists with very little force input.

Natural Frequency, first: The lowest natural frequency of a component.

Natural Frequency, second: The next lowest natural frequency of a component.

Natural Frequencies, higher order: Third, fourth, etc. natural frequencies.

Non-Linear: Any process whose output varies with the input in a non-proportional manner.

Orientation, fiber: The direction of the axis of the fibers in a composite material.

Oscillation: Vibration.

Ovality: The condition of being egg-shaped.

Parabolic: The general shape of the static deflection curve of a fly rod heavily weighted at the tip.

Passivation, surface: A chemical reaction on a metal surface, rendering it less prone to further reaction.

Path, line: The path that the fly line follows during a cast.

Path, rod tip: The path that the fly rod tip follows during a casting stroke.

Pentagon: A 5-sided regular polygon.

Photo, strobe: A series of sequential images obtained using a strobe light source.

Pi (π): The numerical constant, 3.1416, which is the ratio of the circumference of a circle to its diameter.

Pitch: One of three substances commonly used as a precursor in the pyrolysis of graphite fibers.

Plane: A perfectly flat area, with no portions curved nor angled.

Planing Forms: Fixtures used by cane rod makers to hand-plane splines to their final dimensions.

Polyacrylonitrile (PAN): One of three substances commonly used as precursors in the pyrolysis of graphite fibers.

Polygon: A multi-sided, closed planar figure.

Polygon, regular: A polygon having three or more sides of equal length.

Potential Energy: Energy stored in a fly rod as a result of flexure.

Precursor: A substance from which another substance is formed.

Prepreg: A tape consisting of backing paper plus fibers pre-impregnated with a partially-cured resin.

Profile, aerodynamic: The path made by a rod moving through the air during a cast.

Profile, diametral: The variation in outside diameters along the length of a fly rod.

Profile, flexural: The flexural shape of a fly rod while being statically loaded.

Profile, inertial: The variation of unit weight along the length of a fly rod.

Profile, stiffness: The variation of section stiffness along the length of a fly rod.

Profile, stress: The variation of maximum bending stress along the length of a fly rod.

Proportional Limit: The point on the load/deflection curve where further deflection would produce permanent deformation.

Pultrusion: Pulling a group of resin-saturated fibers through a die to produce a green composite rod.

Put-and-Take: An outdated fisheries management philosophy involving matching fish hatchery production to angler consumptive demand.

Pyrolysis: A high temperature treatment used in the production of graphite fibers.

Quadrate: A cane fly rod of square cross-section; i.e. having four equal-width sides.

Radius: The distance between the center and the circumference of a circle.

Rayon: One of the three precursors used in the pyrolysis of graphite fibers.

Reel Seat: A device to attach a fly reel to a fly rod.

Reel Seat, locking A reel seat using one or more devices to lock the reel seat in place.

Reel Seat, skeleton: A locking reel seat with open sections to expose the underlying wood or cork.

Reel Seat, slide band: A reel seat employing one or two slide bands to hold the reel seat feet in place by friction.

Resin, natural: Resins naturally found in wood and cane, which bind the natural fibers in place.

Resin, plastic: A man-made resin, chemically synthesized to bind man-made fibers in place.

Resin, thermoplastic: A plastic resin which, even after curing, can be deformed at high temperature without reducing its mechanical properties.

Resin, thermosetting: A plastic resin which cannot be deformed after curing without compromising its mechanical properties.

Resin-Rich: An area within a fiber composite where there is excess resin.

Resistance, wind: Aerodynamic drag on a body in motion.

Ridge, pattern-edge: The protruding edge of a cured rod tape pattern, insufficiently compacted to keep it within the circumference of a circular cross-section.

Rigidity: A property of a relatively stiff material, or having a high bulk modulus.

Rolling Table: A table with two moving platens, used to roll tape patterns onto mandrels.

Scrim: A very fine denier cloth, used to help maintain fiber/resin position in a prepreg.

Section Geometry: The geometric shape of a fly rod's cross-section.

Shrink-Tape: Cellophane or other tape which shrinks at high temperatures, to compact fiber/resin structures during oven curing.

Shrink-Tubing: Polyolefin or other tubing which shrinks at high temperatures, to compact fiber/resin structures during oven curing.

Spacing, line guide: The location of fly rod line guides, to distribute rod stress from line loads and facilitate line shooting.

Speed: Velocity, especially of a line or fly rod tip.

Spine: An area of an otherwise symmetrical rod which is stiffer than its corresponding segments around the rod.

Spine, effective: The integrated spine of a complete rod or rod section.

Spine, secondary: An additional spine, usually located 180 degrees from the primary spine, caused by the varying tensile and compressive properties of some fiber composites.

Square: A regular polygon having four sides.

Stability: A condition of equilibrium or a steady motion.

Standoff Height, line guide: The distance between the fly rod surface and the ring of the line guide.

Static Conditions: Without movement.

Stiffness: Resistance to deformation. Usually defined as modulus of elasticity, in units of lbs/in^2.

Stiffness, guide foot: The extent to which line guides increase rod section stiffness.

Stiffness, section: The stiffness of a rod cross-section, usually defined as the product of the material's modulus of elasticity and the cross-section's moment of inertia.

Strain: The amount that a material deforms, when subjected to stress.

Stress: The condition of a material or body when subjected to a force or moment.

Stress, bending: The condition of a material or body when subjected to bending or flexure.

Stress, compressive: The condition of a material or body when subjected to compressive forces.

Stress, flexural: Also called bending stress.

Stress, impact: Stress caused by a sudden imposition of force or moment.

Stress, residual: Stress within a material in the absence of any external forces or moments. In fly rods, often caused by curing while bent or by using different fibers having dissimilar thermal coefficients of expansion.

Stress, tensile: The condition of a material or body when subjected to tensile forces.

Stress, torsional: The condition of a material or body when subjected to torsional or twisting forces.

Stress Axis, neutral: That location on a component subjected to flexure, where the local stresses are zero.

Stress Concentration: Local areas of high stress due to significant changes in cross-section or stiffness.

Stressing, over: Stressing a material or component beyond the point where it will perform its intended function.

Strength: The ability of a material to withstand stressing without failure or inelastic deformation.

Strength, compressive: The maximum ability of a material to withstand compressive stresses without failure or inelastic deformation.

Strength, flexural: The maximum ability of a material to withstand flexural stresses without failure or inelastic deformation.

Strength, Hoop: The ability of a component to withstand lateral compressive stresses without failure or inelastic deformation.

Strength, rupture: The stress at which a material will rupture or fail. Also called ultimate strength.

Strength, shear: The maximum ability of a material or component to withstand shear stress without failure or inelastic deformation.

Strength, tensile: The maximum ability of a material or component to withstand tensile stresses without failure or inelastic deformation.

Strength, torsional: The maximum ability of a material or component to withstand torsional stresses without failure or inelastic deformation.

Strength, ultimate: Also called Rupture Strength.

Strength, yield: The stress at which a material will inelastically deform.

Structural Integrity: The condition where a component will successfully perform its intended function without failure or inelastic deformation.

Swing-Weight: A standard classification system for rating a golf club's weight beyond the grip.

Tack, resin: The stickiness of a resin in a prepreg, to determine how well it will self-adhere during layup.

Taper: The variation of a fly rod's outside diameter, inside diameter, stiffness and unit weight along its length.

Testing, cantilever beam: Testing a rod or rod section as if it were a cantilever beam.

Testing, frequency measurement: Testing a fly rod to determine its modes of natural frequency.

Testing, quality assurance: Testing all or a sample of production articles to determine quality levels or trends.

Testing, static deflection: Testing of a fly rod to

determine its flexural curve and its maximum tip deflection.

Testing, stiffness profile: Testing of a fly rod to determine its section stiffness level throughout its length.

Testing, wiggle: Angler wiggling of a fly rod to approximate its first and second natural frequencies.

Thread Wrappings: Winding thread over line guide feet, ferrules, etc to attach them to the fly rod or to improve the rod's cosmetic appearance.

Tip-Top: The line guide at the extreme tip of the fly rod.

Torque: The moment, usually expressed in foot-pounds, applied to the fly rod grip during casting and fish-fighting.

Torsional Stiffness: The ability of a component, especially a golf club shaft, to withstand torsional stress without excessive angular deformation.

Uncoupled: The isolation of one component from others in a vibrating system.

Velocity: The speed of a body or component, usually expressed in units of miles per hour or feet per second.

Vibration Amplitude: The maximum deflection or motion of a vibrating component.

Vibration Frequency: The frequency of a vibrating component or system, usually expressed in cycles per second.

Vibration Mode: The shape of a vibrating system at its maximum amplitude.

Vibration node: Point locations in a vibrating system where there is no motion during vibration.

Void Content: Areas in a fly rod where air or gas bubbles remain after the curing process.

Volume: The total space occupied by a component, usually expressed in cubic inches or cubic centimeters.

Volume Fraction: The volume percent occupied by a constituent in a composite material.

Warp, rod: The undesired curvature of a rod when not under load. Usually caused by residual stresses introduced during curing.

Wear Resistance: The ability of a material to resist wear when subjected to sliding friction.

Weight: The force with which a body is attracted toward the earth by gravity.

Appendix A
BIBLIOGRAPHIES

The following books, papers and magazine articles have been listed by the author because they contain useful information on the technology of fly rods. Within each table the material is listed in the chronological order of their publishing date.

Table A-1, The Earliest Books

1) *The Treatyse of Fysshynge Wyth an Angle*, 1496, by Dame Juliana Berners
2) *The Little Treatise on Fishing*, 1539, by Fernando Basurto
3) *The Arte of Angling*, 1577, by William Samuel
4) *A Book of Fishing With Hooke and Line*, 1590, by Leonard Mascall
5) *Secrets of Angling*, 1613, by John Dennys
6) *Second Book of the English Husbandman*, 1614, by Gervase Markham
7) *The Art of Angling*, 1651, Thomas Barker
8) *The Compleat Angler*, 1653 Edition, by Izaak Walton
9) *Les Ruses Innocentes*, 1660, by Frere Francois Fortin
10) *The Experienced Angler*, 1662, by Robert Venables
11) *The Compleat Angler*, 1676 Edition, by Izaak Walton and Charles Cotton
12) *The Angler's Vade Mecum*, 1681, by Chetham
13) *The Art of Angling* 1747, by Charles Bowlker
14) *The Angler's Museum*, 1784, by Thomas Shirley
15) *The Art of Angling*, 1787, by Thomas Best

Table A-2, Nineteenth Century Books

1) *Practical Observations on Angling in the River Trent*, 1801, Snart
2) *A Handbook of Angling*, 1847, by Edward Fitzgibbon (Ephemera)
3) *The Practical Angler*, 1857, by W.C. Stewart
4) *A Book On Angling*, 1867, by Francis Francis
5) *Anleitung zur Angel-Fischerei*, 1882, by William Bischoff
6) *Fly Rods and Fly Tackle*, 1885, by H.P. Wells
7) *Fishing Tackle*, 1886, by John Harrington Keene
8) *Dry Fly Fishing* 1889, by Frederic Halford
9) *The Book of the Black Bass*, 1889, by James Henshall

Table A-3, Twentieth Century Books

1) *Fly Fishing: Some New Arts and Mysteries*, Undated, by J.C. Mottram
2) *Idyll of the Split Bamboo*, 1920, by George Parker Holden
3) *A History of Fly Fishing For Trout*, 1921, by John Waller Hills
4) *Trout*, 1938, by Ray Bergman
5) *Modern Fly Casting*, 1942, by John Alden Knight
6) *The American Angler*, 1954, by A.J. McClane
7) *The Complete Book of Fly Fishing*, 1958, by Joe Brooks
8) *A Fly Fisher's Life*, 1959, by Charles Ritz
9) *The Origins of Angling*, 1963, by John McDonald
10) *New Standard Fishing Encyclopedia*, 1965, by A.J. McClane
11) *Nymphs*, 1973, by Ernest G. Schwiebert
12) *Fly Fishing Strategy*, 1975, by Doug Swisher and Carl Richards
13) *The Practical Fly Fisherman*, 1975, by A.J. McClane
14) *In The Ring of the Rise*, 1976, by Vincent C. Marinaro
15) *Classic Rods and Rodmakers*, 1976, by Martin J. Keane
16) *Colorado Classic Cane*, 1976, by Dick Spurr and Michael Sinclair
17) *Trout*, 1978, by Ernest G. Schwiebert
18) *Trout Tackle - Part 2*, 1978, by Ernest G. Schwiebert

19) *The Angler's Workshop*, 1979, by Letcher Lambuth
20) *The Atlantic Salmon*, 1983, by Lee Wulff
21) *American Fly Fishing - A History*, 1987, by Paul Schullery
22) *The Essence of Flycasting*, 1987, by Mel Krieger
23) *U.S. Fishing Rod Patents and Other Tackle*, 1990, by Mary Kefover Kelly
24) *Dickerson, The Man and His Rods*, 1991, by Gerald S. Stein and Jim Schaaf
25) *Fiberglass Fly Rods - The Evolution of the Modern Fly Rod from Bamboo to Graphite*, 1996, by Victor R. Johnson and Victor R. Johnson Jr.
26) *Classic Bamboo Rodmakers Past and Present*, 1992, by Dick Spurr
27) *Wes Jordan, Profile of a Rodmaker*, 1992, by Dick Spurr and Gloria Jordan

28) *The Illustrated Encyclopedia of Fly Fishing*, 1993, by Silvio Calabi
29) *Fishing Rods by Divine*, 1993, by Michael Sinclair
30) *The Sporting Craftsmen*, 1995, by Art Carter
31) *The Collector's Guide to Antique Fishing Tackle*, 1996, by Silvio Calabi
32) *Casting Angles*, 1997, by Mac Brown
33) *Antique and Collectible Fishing Rods Identification and Value Guide*, 1997, by D.B. Homel
34) *The Angler's Bamboo*, 1997, by Luis Marden
35) *Fishing Bamboo*, 1997, by John Gierach
36) *Heddon: The Rod With the Fighting Heart*, 1997, by Michael Sinclair
37) *Classic and Antique Fly Fishing Tackle*, 1997, by A.J. Campbell
38) *The Nature of Fly Casting*, 1999, by Jason Borger

Table A-4, Rod-Building Books

1) *Amateur Rod Making*, 1914, by Perry D. Frazier
2) *The Bamboo Rod and How To Build It*, 1951, Claude Kreider
3) *How to Build Your Own Split Cane Fishing Rod*, 1954, by G. Lawton Moss
4) *Fiberglass Rod Making*, 1973, by Don McClain
5) *Fiberglass Rod Making*, 1974, Dale Clemens
6) *Tackle Craft*, 1974, by C. Boyd Pfeiffer
7) *Rod Building*, 1975, by Alan Vare and Ken Whitehead
8) *A Master's Guide to Building A Bamboo Fly Rod*, 1977, by Hoagy B. Carmichael and Everett Garrison
9) *How to Make Bamboo Fly Rods*, 1977, by George W. Barnes
10) *How To Make Your Own Fishing Rods*, 1978, by Mel Marshall
11) *New Advanced Custom Rod Building*, 1978, by Dale Clemens
12) *Custom Rod Thread Art*, 1982, by Dale Clemens
13) *Rod Building And Repair*, 1984, Len Head

14) *Do-It-Yourself Rod Building*, by Bill Stinson
15) *The Fine Bamboo Fly Rod, A Master's Secrets of Restoration and Repair*, 1986, by Stuart Kirkfield
16) *The Custom Graphite Rod, Design and Construction*, 1989, by Skip Morris
17) *Handcrafting Bamboo Fly Rods*, 1992, by Wayne Cattanach
18) *Bamboo Rod Restoration Handbook*, 1994, by Michael Sinclair
19) *Handcrafting a Graphite Fly Rod*, 1994, by Luis Garcia
20) *Graphite Rod Repair*, 1997, by Luis Garcia
21) *The Best of the Planing Form*, 1997, by R.L. Barch and Robert McKeon
22) *The Lovely Reed, An Enthusiast's Guide to Building Bamboo Fly Rods*, 1998 by Jack Howell
23) *Fundamentals of Building a Bamboo Fly Rod*, 1998, by George Maurer and Bernard Elser
24) *Constructing Cane Rods: Secrets of the Bamboo Fly Rod*, 1999, by Ray Gould

Table A-5, Fly-Fishing Magazine Articles

From 1959 through 1998, over 15,000 articles were published in 14 different fly-fishing magazines. For many years the author maintained an electronic database of all of these articles, to accompany my complete collection of nearly 900 magazines. In September 1998, this collection and database was donated to the American Museum of Fly Fishing, who plans to maintain it and keep it up to date. Using this database, I was able to identify those magazine articles which included information on fly rods.

Of the total of 15,021 magazine articles, 552 or 4% contained information on fly rods. Of these, nearly half related to fly rod history and another third related to rod building. Of the remainder, I identified sixty-eight articles which contained useful technical information on either fly rods or fly-casting. These articles are tabulated in the following list:

Article Title	Author	Magazine	Pg.	Issue
1. Another Dimension For Fly Rod Evaluation - Stiffness Profile	Don Phillips	*Fly Fisherman*	2	June/July 1973
2. A New Era of Fibers For Fly Rods	Don Phillips	*Fly Fisherman*	34	December 1973
3. New Technical Development In Fly Rod Design	Phil Clock	*Fly Fisherman*	36	March 1974
4. A Longer Look at Graphite	Alan Pratt	*Flyfisher*	20	October 1974
5. Graphite - The Rod Material Of the Future?	Mark Sosin	*Fly Fisherman*	36	May 1975
6. What's New in Fishing Rods?	George W. Linnane	*Trout*	16	Spring 1976
7. Patents	Ruth W. Upson	*American Fly Fisher*	6	Winter 1977
8. Fiberglass Fly Rods	Mark Sosin	*Fly Fisherman*	70	January 1978
9. Fly Rod Action and Taper Design	Hoagy B. Carmichael	*Fly Fisherman*	94	January 1978
10. Where the Action Was . . . And Is	Dick Finlay	*Fly Fisherman*	83	April 1978
11. The Long Rod	J. Barry Lloyd	*Flyfishing*	31	December 1978
12. How to Cast the Wrong Line On the Right Rod	Dick Finlay	*Fly Fisherman*	104	May 1979
13. Boron/Graphite Rods	Dick Finlay	*Fly Fisherman*	109	May 1979
14. The Chaos in Components	C. Boyd Pfeiffer	*Fly Rod & Reel*	54	Sept/Oct 1979
15. Evaluating Ceramic Guides	Staff	*Fly Rod & Reel*	58	Sept/Oct 1979
16. The Zinger Trend: A Square Rod For Free Thinkers	Don Roberts	*Flyfishing*	38	October 1979
17. Boron	Silvio A. Calabi	*Fly Rod & Reel*	15	Nov/Dec 1979
18. Boron Rods	Ernest Schwiebert	*Fly Fisherman*	32	Spring 1980
19. On Defining Fly Rod Actions	Bruce Bowlen	*Fly Rod & Reel*	48	Sept/Oct 1980
20. The Dynamics of a Fly Cast	Ed Mosser and William W. Buchman	*Flyfisher*	5	October 1980
21. On Casting-Rod Actions	Jerry Gibbs	*Fly Rod & Reel*	40	Jan/Feb 1981
22. Progressive-Taper Fly Rods	Dick Finlay	*Fly Fisherman*	74	May/June 1981
23. Is Boron Really Better?	Silvio Calabi	*Fly Rod & Reel*	38	May/June 1981
24. Different Strokes	Don Phillips	*Fly Rod & Reel*	12	Mar/Apr 1982
25. When Your Fly Rod Fits	Dick Pobst	*Fly Rod & Reel*	28	Mar/Apr 1982
26. Fly Rod Actions	Dave Engerbretson	*Fly Rod & Reel*	38	Mar/Apr 1982
27. Fly-Casting Grips	Ed Mosser	*Fly Rod & Reel*	32	Nov/Dec 1982
28. Boron Up-Date	Dave Engerbretson	*Fly Fisherman*	54	May 1983
29. Home-Built Fiber Rods	Don Phillips	*Fly Rod & Reel*	22	May/June 1984

Table A-6, Technical Papers on Fly Rods or Fly-Casting

The author is very grateful to Graig Spolek for his permission to reproduce this reference list.

1. *On the Deflection of a Cantilever Beam*, Quarterly of Applied Mathematics, V.2 (2) , pp 168-171, 1944, by H. J. Barten
2. *Large Deflections of Cantilever Beams*, Quarterly of Applied Mathematics, V.3 (3) , pp 272-275, 1945, by K.R. Bisshopp and D.C. Drucker
3. *On the Dynamics of a Bull Whip*, Journal of the Acoustic Society of America, V.30, (12), pp 1112-1115, 1958, by B. Bernstein, D.A. Hall, and H.M. Trent
4. *On the Large Amplitude Oscillations of a Thin Elastic Beam*, International Journal of Non-Linear Mechanics, V.1, pp 217-238, 1966, by S.R. Woodall
5. *Chebyshev Approximation Applied to Large Deflections of Elastica*, Journal of Industrial Mathematics Society, V.18, (2), pp 63-74, 1968, by H.H. Denman and R. Schmidt
6. *An Analysis of Casting Action of Selected Fly Rods*, Department of Physical Education, Pennsylvania State University, 1968, by D.L. Engerbretson
7. *Nonlinear Transverse Vibrations of Beams with Properties that Vary Along the Length*, Journal of the Acoustic Society of America, V.53, (3), pp 766-770, 1973, by A.H. Nayfeh
8. *Variational Formulation of Non-Linear Equations for Straight Elastic Beams*, Journal of Industrial Mathematics Society, V.23, (2), pp 117-136, 1973, by R. Schmidt and D.A. DaDeppo
9. *Nonlinear Analysis of the Forced Response of Structural Elements*, Journal of the Acoustic Society of America, V.55, (2), pp 281-291, 1974, by A.H. Nayfeh, D.T. Mook and S. Sridhar
10. *Nonlinear Vibrations of Non-Uniform Beams with Concentrated Masses*, Journal of Sound Vibration, V.33, (1), pp 1-12, 1974, by M.K. Verma and A.V.K. Murthy
11. *Nonlinear Vibrations of Tapered Cantilevers*, Journal of Sound Vibration, V.55, (1), pp 1-8, 1977, by G. Prathap and T.K. Varadan
12. *The Role of Saint Venant's Solution in Rod and Beam Theories*, Journal of Applied Mathematics, V.46, pp 861-866, 1979, by D.F. Parker
13. *Nonlinear Free Vibrations of Inextensible Beams*, Journal of Sound Vibration, V.64, (1), 1979, by K. Takahashi
14. *Large Deflections and Large-Amplitude Free Vibrations of Straight and Curved Beams*, International Journal of Numerical Methods Engineering, V.17, (6), pp 829-852, 1981, by J.N. Reddy and I.R. Singh
15. *Casting Principles and Dynamics*, (Unpublished), V.1, 1981 and V.2, 1982, by D. Le Breton
16. *Analysis of Large Deflections of Fishing Rods*, Proceedings of the International Conference on Computational Methods and Experimental Measurements, pp 637-648, 1982 by G.A. Spolek and S.R. Jeffries
17. *Theoretical and Practical Aspects of Energy Storage and Compression*, Lawrence Livermore Laboratory, 1983, by O.S.F. Zucker and W.H. Bostick
18. *Simple Line Motion Model*, (Unpublished), 1984, by D. Le Breton
19. *The Lumped Mass Method for Predicting the Fundamental Frequency of Fly Rods*, 1985, Unpublished, by G.A. Spolek
20. *The Large Deformation Analysis of Graphite Fishing Rods*, Computers and Structures, V.21, No. 112, pp 265-271, 1985, by H. Ohnishi and A. Matsuzaki
21. *On the Dynamics of Flexible Beams Under Large Overall Motion - The Plane Case, Part II*, Journal of Applied Mathematics, V.53, pp 855-862, 1986, by J.C. Simo and L. Vu-Quoc
22. *The Mechanics of Flycasting: The Flyline*, American Journal of Physics, V.54, (9), pp 832-836, 1986, by G.A. Spolek
23. *The Mechanics of Flycasting Equipment*, Biomechanics in Sport - A, 1987 Update, American Society of Mechanical Engineers, DE-V.13, pp 23-26, 1987 by G.A. Spolek
22. *Note on the Aerodynamics of a Flyline*, American Journal of Physics, V.56, (8), 1988, by S. Lingard
23. *The Physics of Fly Casting*, American Journal of Physics, V.58, (3), pp 234-240, 1990, by J.M. Robson
24. *The Dynamics of Fly Lines and Other Classical Strings*, B.A. Thesis, Division of Mathematics and Natural Sciences, Reed College, 1992, by Christopher Barnes
25. *Fly Rod Performance, Advances in Bioengineering*, American Society of Mechanical Engineers, BED V.26, pp 251-254, by G.A. Spolek
26. *Dynamic Modeling of Tapered Multi-Sectional Flexible Fly Rods*, Master's Thesis, Clemson University, 1996, by R.D. Haun

Appendix B
U.S. FISHING ROD PATENTS

The following tables list the numbers of all US patents issued between April 18, 1854 and December 31, 1998 that relate to fishing rods (USPTO Class 43, Subclasses 18 through 26), excluding the more trivial ones related to strike indicators, rod holders, etc.

Table B-1
FISHING RODS (GENERAL) AND BLANKS

119,251	1,336,088	1,972,518	2,452,788	2,735,208	3,088,239	3,416,256	3,717,947	4,157,181	4,738,046	5,245,779
164,828	1,337,378	1,984,644	2,465,744	2,742,728	3,102,358	3,417,500	3,727,338	4,162,587	4,747,227	5,259,140
230,650	1,371,261	2,017,303	2,478,131	2,746,198	3,121,290	3,421,247	3,732,644	4,183,163	4,759,147	5,276,990
250,842	1,385,149	2,088,132	2,483,071	2,749,643	3,129,525	3,421,248	3,744,173	4,200,126	4,805,336	5,291,683
330,572	1,406,268	2,089,744	2,496,403	2,758,407	3,142,127	3,431,670	3,754,346	4,209,931	4,821,447	5,295,322
336,255	1,441,045	2,104,494	2,504,631	2,759,288	3,165,855	3,432,958	3,778,916	4,212,126	4,839,981	5,299,377
359,153	1,442,813	2,158,932	2,536,388	2,775,838	3,168,789	3,435,551	3,789,533	4,218,841	4,854,068	5,311,695
372,165	1,494,530	2,159,795	2,537,488	2,775,838	3,172,226	3,436,857	3,791,063	4,237,639	4,860,481	5,317,828
386,320	1,593,957	2,180,323	2,538,306	2,777,239	3,210,881	3,436,858	3,798,823	4,355,061	4,860,482	5,328,742
386,321	1,625,510	2,196,742	2,538,338	2,778,239	3,216,144	3,445,952	3,813,807	4,422,259	4,870,774	5,369,904
395,931	1,643,003	2,196,743	2,541,609	2,781,602	3,217,442	3,447,254	3,835,569	4,432,155	4,878,309	5,375,364
475,852	1,740,908	2,210,231	2,541,759	2,796,358	3,222,813	3,452,468	3,899,846	4,443,963	4,884,356	5,381,619
476,370	1,748,223	2,216,341	2,559,934	2,808,676	3,245,170	3,461,593	3,953,637	4,464,856	4,885,865	5,406,736
592,613	1,752,397	2,218,045	2,566,647	2,851,811	3,260,010	3,465,464	3,955,303	4,467,549	4,903,427	5,479,740
638,733	1,755,159	2,225,714	2,571,692	2,893,158	3,279,115	3,466,783	3,956,845	4,468,270	4,962,608	5,488,797
692,884	1,811,419	2,230,229	2,571,717	2,904,920	3,279,116	3,468,051	3,956,846	4,501,085	5,048,223	5,538,769
706,225	1,843,714	2,239,227	2,577,575	2,932,111	3,295,244	3,469,338	3,975,855	4,516,351	5,060,412	5,564,214
735,471	1,844,044	2,276,524	2,578,663	2,933,845	3,314,186	3,500,570	4,003,778	4,520,587	5,071,687	5,575,103
785,845	1,870,976	2,282,233	2,593,885	2,958,975	3,315,400	3,500,571	4,015,360	4,541,197	5,076,004	5,577,338
813,492	1,871,229	2,282,618	2,594,536	2,972,204	3,390,479	3,507,069	4,020,581	4,582,758	5,115,591	5,592,771
849,481	1,874,246	2,292,519	2,597,738	3,000,129	3,392,473	3,513,582	4,024,666	4,601,127	5,125,147	5,592,772
911,119	1,880,348	2,296,174	2,600,259	3,001,316	3,394,485	3,525,174	4,043,071	4,627,188	5,175,952	5,704,157
912,552	1,914,500	2,302,191	2,610,427	3,003,275	3,400,480	3,557,483	4,043,074	4,648,195	5,188,152	5,713,151
1,020,044	1,927,724	2,306,638	2,620,586	3,010,242	3,400,481	3,570,164	4,057,926	4,649,661	5,189,824	5,721,030
1,098,769	1,932,986	2,324,429	2,628,445	3,015,182	3,401,480	3,579,896	4,061,806	4,653,215	5,193,298	5,806,230
1,231,150	1,944,503	2,341,053	2,632,273	3,026,644	3,401,481	3,581,425	4,075,776	4,653,216	5,194,207	5,806,231
1,283,015	1,961,642	2,344,533	2,662,329	3,036,398	3,401,482	3,581,427	4,084,343	4,654,994	5,197,218	5,826,366
1,310,452	1,961,968	2,345,043	2,680,923	3,052,055	3,413,748	3,618,253	4,121,369	4,685,241	5,231,785	5,829,182
1,318,421	1,961,969	2,351,734	2,709,315	3,060,617	3,415,002	3,656,252	4,142,317	4,686,787	5,239,768	5,832,653
1,324,554	1,961,970	2,421,240	2,724,203	3,065,563	3,416,255	3,691,000	4,151,672	4,693,029	5,241,773	

Table B-2
ROD/REEL COMBINATIONS

43,546	357,988	491,955	664,786	970,356	1,377,787	1,742,645	2,217,820	2,561,237	2,772,505	3,006,098	3,641,695
49,663	369,622	495,827	669,332	977,732	1,415,310	1,763,934	2,342,993	2,569,604	2,781,602	3,020,665	3,685,195
96,652	379,683	515,184	681,687	1,005,015	1,497,364	1,955,973	2,352,903	2,584,020	2,849,824	3,040,463	3,745,684
166,241	384,672	527,713	713,633	1,010,021	1,538,377	2,028,311	2,381,089	2,584,678	2,861,379	3,064,385	3,789,535
175,227	412,629	529,658	733,836	1,062,488	1,544,128	2,100,428	2,394,706	2,599,219	2,864,197	3,069,800	3,803,745
195,578	415,322	558,821	734,870	1,111,340	1,558,310	2,141,817	2,399,863	2,628,444	2,875,548	3,229,406	3,836,921
208,500	436,302	577,664	739,784	1,119,474	1,572,104	2,144,635	2,402,882	2,664,661	2,896,354	3,269,049	4,905,399
227,000	460,272	610,880	769,142	1,150,575	1,605,710	2,158,396	2,409,098	2,671,289	2,908,102	3,296,732	5,199,206
254,025	465,254	641,906	786,639	1,256,389	1,607,285	2,172,389	2,410,331	2,674,057	2,943,413	3,302,320	5,237,770
283,084	465,579	643,538	787,055	1,263,939	1,632,522	2,178,120	2,494,952	2,703,466	2,948,078	3,310,904	5,519,958
303,347	468,180	646,085	865,613	1,270,726	1,640,350	2,179,413	2,501,530	2,716,301	2,952,091	3,325,938	5,577,679
335,797	472,263	646,737	868,722	1,285,679	1,648,824	2,182,423	2,541,876	2,729,012	2,957,264	3,405,473	
335,798	472,766	651,639	889,974	1,319,268	1,735,026	2,190,984	2,548,102	2,752,717	2,965,995	3,491,475	
346,490	484,439	657,518	892,137	1,327,751	1,738,204	2,194,639	2,548,224	2,765,568	2,976,640	3,618,252	

Table B-3
ROD HANDLES, BUTTS AND GRIPS

10,795	848,243	1,448,120	2,057,535	2,236,603	2,482,192	2,628,446	2,955,376	3,418,742	4,424,639	4,697,377	5,363,587
137,015	887,753	1,452,808	2,065,153	2,252,054	2,483,519	2,655,756	3,014,306	3,443,335	4,453,332	4,762,584	5,396,727
206,264	931,277	1,458,057	2,084,931	2,260,204	2,484,223	2,673,416	3,047,974	3,451,156	4,467,548	4,780,980	5,426,884
250,204	942,030	1,587,446	2,085,654	2,283,816	2,485,144	2,685,755	3,058,253	3,468,052	4,498,257	4,793,087	5,509,228
250,968	967,642	1,641,226	2,116,158	2,289,216	2,495,980	2,699,622	3,068,603	3,499,241	4,528,769	4,796,373	5,524,376
270,460	980,942	1,731,173	2,144,122	2,315,539	2,502,608	2,711,045	3,073,055	3,500,572	4,577,432	4,817,324	5,535,539
394,032	1,001,326	1,839,751	2,149,837	2,409,988	2,504,801	2,711,046	3,080,673	3,531,888	4,578,890	4,848,022	5,537,773
396,909	1,013,333	1,898,323	2,152,385	2,422,084	2,514,950	2,737,747	3,175,321	3,570,165	4,584,787	4,850,130	5,551,184
461,106	1,033,668	1,916,924	2,177,064	2,424,430	2,522,624	2,753,646	3,175,323	3,950,883	4,598,192	4,858,365	5,557,875
549,292	1,056,870	1,920,966	2,177,433	2,431,972	2,526,080	2,756,531	3,181,264	3,973,348	4,631,853	4,860,483	5,581,931
583,016	1,113,847	1,923,035	2,182,901	2,433,197	2,526,293	2,761,236	3,213,563	3,982,348	4,646,460	4,916,852	5,797,554
764,398	1,271,073	1,931,303	2,186,515	2,435,404	2,534,027	2,776,516	3,222,811	4,014,129	4,646,461	4,920,682	5,845,428
797,637	1,276,780	1,962,869	2,187,807	2,443,567	2,547,655	2,776,516	3,276,160	4,020,825	4,648,196	5,231,782	
814,321	1,302,457	2,000,263	2,206,019	2,443,946	2,554,787	2,795,073	3,309,809	4,077,150	4,651,461	5,263,275	
819,500	1,318,085	2,003,893	2,208,493	2,447,720	2,559,933	2,805,508	3,410,016	4,130,960	4,654,996	5,291,684	
828,557	1,351,473	2,010,627	2,219,474	2,454,529	2,565,633	2,830,399	3,410,017	4,190,977	4,688,346	5,337,507	
841,761	1,375,668	2,018,923	2,226,897	2,456,681	2,583,909	2,839,864	3,411,230	4,229,898	4,697,376	5,338,604	

Table B-4
REEL SEATS & OTHER ATTACHMENT MEANS

235,017	553,725	888,075	1,494,552	1,827,277	2,027,243	2,166,407	2,517,224	2,782,547	3,197,908	3,616,563	4,702,032
235,511	651,148	905,428	1,500,390	1,831,738	2,029,188	2,182,409	2,543,881	2,782,547	3,226,873	3,616,564	4,726,139
235,512	718,589	950,656	1,510,906	1,837,623	2,034,901	2,194,029	2,546,341	2,787,857	3,229,405	3,616,565	4,845,882
235,513	773,703	951,731	1,534,674	1,870,078	2,038,344	2,198,588	2,592,109	2,808,675	3,233,355	3,653,141	4,860,484
258,902	790,419	953,775	1,591,035	1,879,795	2,069,977	2,198,856	2,592,878	2,814,147	3,364,612	3,698,118	4,891,899
294,429	820,685	1,035,936	1,591,122	1,897,889	2,076,628	2,260,885	2,593,747	2,837,858	3,372,509	3,792,546	5,033,225
303,186	831,764	1,041,376	1,617,951	1,902,749	2,089,538	2,325,457	2,612,714	2,839,863	3,372,510	3,883,978	5,222,319
331,380	832,307	1,065,481	1,624,052	1,909,529	2,102,237	2,379,578	2,616,204	2,855,718	3,419,992	4,133,133	5,392,556
376,260	834,554	1,159,466	1,644,429	1,970,348	2,104,495	2,400,007	2,630,647	2,885,816	3,426,466	4,187,633	
402,594	834,555	1,339,238	1,698,341	1,970,641	2,111,080	2,409,940	2,656,639	2,926,450	3,461,594	4,403,439	
426,616	837,565	1,350,635	1,711,248	1,980,316	2,114,107	2,479,952	2,667,713	2,967,370	3,501,859	4,439,945	
434,793	849,231	1,350,636	1,745,398	1,980,317	2,120,467	2,487,346	2,749,644	3,074,198	3,512,293	4,494,333	
481,941	858,881	1,350,637	1,752,027	1,994,449	2,131,819	2,490,584	2,777,240	3,098,313	3,522,674	4,554,755	
486,802	863,676	1,367,272	1,785,027	1,995,242	2,143,289	2,498,648	2,777,240	3,123,931	3,564,752	4,637,157	
506,607	878757	1,464,154	1,820,781	2,020,869	2,145,612	2,503,510	2,780,883	3,196,572	3,581,426	4,696,123	

Table B-5
GUIDES & TIP-TOPS

20,309	396,707	814,431	1,157,106	1,959,989	2,293,280	2,596,835	2,778,141	3,165,856	3,760,524	4,215,504	5,181,336
25,693	406,465	839,104	1,409,282	1,984,349	2,306,112	2,623,317	2,778,141	3,171,228	3,769,735	4,277,906	5,283,973
35,339	506,093	863,606	1,444,063	2,038,175	2,317,129	2,650,447	2,792,660	3,171,229	3,769,736	4,287,678	5,347,743
58,833	521,704	868,563	1,473,437	2,113,707	2,319,462	2,652,654	2,805,509	3,222,812	3,797,158	4,334,379	5,361,529
173,534	564,742	899,914	1,478,643	2,147,063	2,324,353	2,697,894	2,863,252	3,256,633	3,997,997	4,454,676	5,417,007
198,879	638,733	919,778	1,595,275	2,197,245	2,360,802	2,702,959	2,872,751	3,303,595	4,011,680	4,507,891	5,419,075
234,812	670,961	958,775	1,627,643	2,197,358	2,398,862	2,718,085	2,880,546	3,350,809	4,030,224	4,586,285	5,448,850
263,484	676,554	1,063,402	1,781,569	2,199,861	2,484,727	2,724,204	3,058,254	3,354,574	4,051,618	4,616,438	5,456,038
277,230	682,730	1,073,260	1,835,310	2,216,002	2,502,845	2,740,221	3,058,255	3,402,500	4,070,785	4,682,439	5,467,932
338,212	703,996	1,078,589	1,856,551	2,226,295	2,502,846	2,741,412	3,060,618	3,403,468	4,141,132	4,807,385	5,491,881
343,802	734,544	1,116,721	1,917,493	2,227,868	2,514,929	2,760,292	3,063,186	3,417,501	4,156,319	4,888,906	5,560,139
358,420	754,094	1,141,684	1,923,263	2,231,053	2,544,238	2,762,154	3,067,537	3,641,696	4,176,488	4,891,899	5,570,535
364,350	796,342	1,142,796	1,937,972	2,263,300	2,561,675	2,763,083	3,099,889	3,690,027	4,178,713	4,893,429	5,802,759
387,545	801,884	1,149,131	1,945,068	2,280,759	2,573,647	2,775,054	3,117,388	3,702,514	4,186,508	5,090,150	

Table B-6
FERRULES, JOINTS AND SPLICES

72,667	222,681	337,474	422,470	499,779	837,157	998,318	1,527,463	2,793,458	3,609,906	4,138,301	4,860,485
100,895	252,008	337,589	427,162	505,579	895,372	1,033,430	2,005,081	2,816,399	3,613,287	4,160,607	5,528,848
108,679	264,243	339,204	428,755	537,088	902,673	1,064,030	2,293,559	2,902,789	3,947,141	4,362,418	
140,656	303,474	346,605	467,979	613,903	931,277	1,450,799	2,334,646	3,186,122	4,029,424	4,441,274	
169,181	322,750	373,561	470,473	719,603	984,741	1,512,509	2,365,414	3,245,169	4,070,127	4,575,277	
207,665	324,450	406,465	475,024	799,810	990,599	1,524,590	2,546,079	3,310,903	4,083,140	4,768,303	

Index